# AN ILLUSTRATED GUIDE TO
# SPY PLANES
## and Electronic Warfare Aircraft

a Salamander book

Published by Salamander Books Limited
LONDON

# AN ILLUSTRATED GUIDE TO
# SPY PLANES
## and Electronic Warfare Aircraft

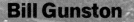

U.S. AIR FORCE

**Bill Gunston**

# A Salamander Book

© 1983 Salamander Books Ltd.,
Salamander House,
27 Old Gloucester Street,
London WC1N 3AF,
United Kingdom.

**ISBN 0 86101 1775**

Distributed in the United Kingdom
by Hodder & Stoughton Services,
PO Box 6, Mill Road,
Dunton Green, Sevenoaks,
Kent TN13 2XX.

# Contents

# Credits

**Author:** Bill Gunston is an Assistant Compiler of *Jane's All The World's Aircraft*, former Technical Editor of *Flight International*, contributor to many technical aerospace journals and author of several other titles in this series.

**Managing Editor:** Ray Bonds.
**Editor/Designer:** Roger Chesneau.

**Diagrams:** TIGA.
**Three-view line drawings:**
© Pilot Press Ltd.

**Colour profiles:**
© Salamander Books Ltd.
and Pilot Press Ltd.
**Filmset** by Modern Text Typesetting Ltd.
**Colour reproduction** by
Rodney Howe Ltd.
**Printed** in Belgium by
Henri Proost et Cie.

**Photographs:** The publishers wish to thank all the official governmental archives, aircraft and system manufacturers, and private individuals, who have supplied photographs for this book.

# Introduction

We are all familiar with books about fighters, bombers and other kinds of combat aircraft. Reconnaissance and electronic warfare seem, by comparison, to be somehow secondary—aircraft designed to fly these missions usually have no guns, bombs or missiles. Yet in any real war a single sortie by one of these aircraft may well prove crucial to a campaign or to the war itself. Intelligence, the general term for information about one's enemies, is absolutely central to weapons, to policies, to strategic and tactical decisions and to overall military posture.

Intelligence is gathered by men in shabby raincoats and by alluring women, by avid reading of the published media and by a score of other channels; but increasingly the most important method is to look down from above. Lifting the vantage point above the Earth's surface enables us to see further. Virtually all the sensors noted in this book operate in various parts of the EM (electromagnetic) spectrum, which includes visible light, radio and radar waves, and IR (infra-red) radiation, commonly known as heat. All such radiation travels in straight lines, though because of ionized layers in the atmosphere some radio waves are reflected great distances around the Earth. Such waves are used for broadcasting, but not for gathering much

Left: World War II aerial cameras were in the main merely bigger versions of ordinary roll-film cameras, though many had remote control, heating and a powered system for winding on the film. Here an RAF tradesman is holding what looks like an F.24 camera, a common type used for both fixed (vertical or oblique) sprung mounting or for handheld use, aimed like a gun with a viewfinder. A few cameras of this period had multiple lenses (in most cases seven) to give one vertical image surrounded by six obliques. The resulting prints were re-photographed in a special machine to correct distortion.

**Right: Modern high-speed aircraft use cameras installed in the airframe, usually aligned on a fixed axis, though in some cases the camera can be manoeuvred for horizon-to-horizon coverage. Here a USAF ground crewman is seen fitting a camera into an RF-4C.**

intelligence. For all practical purposes, the sensors 'see' along straight lines, which we call the line of sight (LOS).

Of course, we live in an age in which aeroplanes can fly great distances across the Earth. They are no longer puny things; for example, on the day this was written Finnair opened a service non-stop from Helsinki to Tokyo. But it is often important to gather information without crossing a particular frontier, so LOS distances become important. Very roughly, the distance we can see — assuming we are in the middle of a calm ocean, and ignoring distortion caused by refraction in the atmosphere — is $d = \sqrt{1.5h}$ where $d$ is the distance in miles and $h$ is our height above sea level in feet. Thus a 6ft (1.83m) man can see approximately 3 miles. Put him in a helicopter and climb to $66\frac{2}{3}$ft (20.3m) and his horizon stretches back to 10 miles. From a radar-equipped aircraft orbiting at 35,000ft (10.7km), the horizon is no less than 230 miles (370km) distant. The minimum practical height for reconnaissance satellites is about 100 miles (161km), and they can "see" about 890 miles (1,432km).

To some, such as the small boy trying to watch a football game from outside the fence, a few feet can make all the difference. The very first time an aircraft was used in warfare was when a French observer, Captain J.M.J. Coutelle, went up in his captive balloon at the Battle of Fleurus on 26 June 1794 and played a crucial role in the defeat by the Army of the Moselle of numerically much stronger Allied forces. Aeroplanes were first used in war on 23 October 1911 when Italian Captain Piazza spent an hour in his Blériot making notes on the Turkish positions between Azizia (El Aziz) and Tripoli. On 24 February 1912 the same pilot made the first aerial reconnaissance sortie using a camera, which in those days was a cumbersome box that completely filled the pilot's lap.

Prior to World War I, reconnaissance was the only role that could be envisaged for aeroplanes in war (airships, in contrast, were thought capable of dropping bombs). It occurred to some people that when aeroplanes engaged on reconnaissance missions met their enemy counterparts doing the same thing, some kind of combat might ensue, ▶

**Above: Oblique of Los Angeles; distance from aircraft to print centre, 10¼ miles (16.5km).**

**Above: Portion of the same photograph enlarged × 4, showing major road intersection.**

▶but this belief was generally scorned as ridiculous fantasy. In fact, of course, air combat soon became very real indeed, while air reconnaissance by 1918 was the full-time task of more than 90,000 people on all fronts, who produced roughly 12,000 large photographic prints a day with a quality and reliability unimagined four years earlier. The pressure of four years of war had transformed aerial reconnaissance into a routine operation using extremely large but very good cameras designed for the job. Some were still hand-held, but the largest were fixed to the aircraft as "vertical" or as

"oblique" (pointing diagonally forward or to one side).

Special mention should be made of Sidney Cotton, an Australian pilot in the RNAS in World War I who in the 1930s became one of the principals of the Dufaycolour company, one of the pioneers of colour film. He was the ideal person to carry out clandestine photo-reconnaissance missions, because of his flying ability, his wide knowledge of cameras and film and his ideal business "cover". He was approached first by the French, who fitted his Lockheed with giant reconnaissance cameras and then refused to let him see the results

**Right: Missions of the TR-1. In the surveillance role the TR-1 can cover 263,014 sq miles (681,170km²) per hour from 65,000ft (19.8km). Passive receivers are used to pinpoint hostile emitters. The two right-hand diagrams show the coverage in EO (TV) imaging and synthetic aperture (phased-array) radar missions. At its ceiling of 90,000ft (20.4km) the TR-1 can see to a distance of 316 miles (507km) in all directions.**

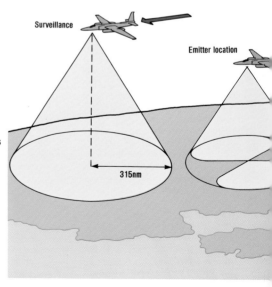

Surveillance

Emitter location

315nm

**Above: Portion of the same photograph enlarged x 16, with local detail appearing.**

**Above: Portion of the same photograph enlarged x 48, about the limit for good definition.**

because they were secret. He got on better with the British, and his gaily painted Lockheed 12A, G-AFTL, soon became a familiar sight from Heston to the Red Sea. Not only did it have a triple fan of large f24 cameras, but in the outer wings were two small Leica 35mm cameras— then a completely new item on the market, the forerunner of the 35mm cameras of today— which with the skin hatches closed were undetectable.

Throughout July and most of August 1939 the Lockheed flew over Germany on perfectly legitimate business, on occasion with high-ranking German guests on board, whilst gathering a marvellous series of high-quality pictures of German airfields, factories and the Siegfried Line of fortifications. Moreover, although the RAF had tried to get good photographs of German targets from the very day World War II began (3 September 1939), and had for a variety of reasons consistently failed, Cotton calmly went out in his civilian Lockheed on 16 September and brought back complete and pin-sharp coverage of the German fleet!

Cotton went on to set up the Photographic Development Unit at Heston, and this became the▶

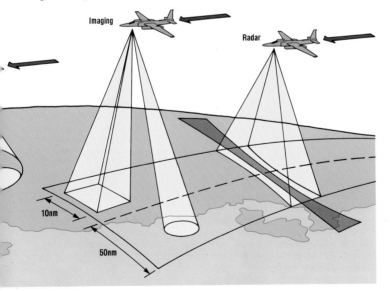

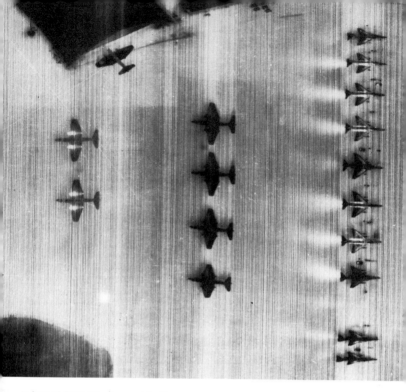

▶famed PRU (Photographic Reconnaissance Unit) which developed not only millions of films but also new techniques and new aircraft. PRU blue, officially Cerulean blue, was a low-visibility colour similar to today's all-grey schemes used on fighters. It was applied not only to aircraft designed to fly in the lower reaches of the stratosphere —not so much to get wider coverage, for the geometrical reasons explained earlier, as to try to avoid being intercepted by hostile fighters—but also to a completely new species of low-flying reconnaissance aircraft based on the fastest fighters but trading weapons for extra fuel and speed, and with cameras mounted behind the cockpit looking sideways. High-speed, low-level photography became a standard technique from late 1940, and it was soon partnered by automatic photographs taken by bombers at the calculated time when their large photoflash bomb and main bomb-load were all exploding on target (or, more often in 1941, not on target).

One of the first, if not the very first, targets of an RAF low-level photo sortie was an enemy radar system. Thanks to this, the very same radar was soon to become the target of a daring British paratroop raid which brought back vital parts of it to England. Thus the British "boffins"—the contemporary term for back-room scientists on whom success in war was increasingly coming to depend—were able to find out the waveform, frequency, PRF (pulse-repetition frequency) and other basic parameters of the equipment and, armed with this knowledge, they were able to devise ways of jamming enemy radars of this type, thus opening up a whole new chapter in warfare.

Today EW (electronic warfare) is as important as bullets and missiles. So evenly balanced has the battle of the electrons become that many of the physicists, electronics engineers and aircrews caught up in it feel it would be nice to abandon the lot and go back to the "Mark I human eyeball". To do so, however, would certainly cause difficulties, because modern aircraft packed ▶

Left: A printout from an IRLS (infra-red linescan), actually a British Aerospace Type 401. RAF Phantoms and Canberras are seen parked on a hardstand. Dark areas are cooler and white areas hotter. Thus the two Canberras on the left have just parked, or been running their engines for a long period to make the cowlings hot. Some of the Phantoms have also been running either one or both engines. Hot concrete has been warmed by ground running, and in the Phantom line a dark patch shows the "shadow" of cool concrete left by an aircraft that has recently taxied out.

Below: Another Linescan Type 401 pattern of heated water (white) from an industrial plant or power station (US = electric utility) dispersing into cool water.

Below: Flat rectangles on the sides of this RC-135C are giant side-looking radars. Did the Russians really think the South Korean Boeing 747, shot down in September 1983, was one of these aircraft?

11

**Above left: The US Navy used the E-1B Tracer as its AEW aircraft from 1959 until 1965.**

**Left: Today's E-3 (AWACS) has eight times the area coverage and a million times more computer power than the E-1B.**

**Above: Inside each AWACS aircraft are nine of these MPCs (multipurpose consoles), on which are displayed computer-processed pictures and information showing an entire tactical situation out to a radius of about 250 miles.**

with electronic devices advertise their presence just as boldly as if they were festooned with lights like a Christmas tree. The silent, or passive, aircraft may lack a lot of useful devices, but it poses immense problems to the enemy.

An oft-told story is that of the Luftwaffe night fighter pilot who in 1944 was posted to the West to help stem the onslaught of the RAF and USAF. He said he found it a very welcome change after being on the Eastern Front. "You see", he said, "the Russians are so backward they have no radar, and that makes it very difficult for us". In other words, to each amazing, war-winning invention there soon comes a counter-invention, and occasionally the new invention plus the counter makes the situation worse than it was before. EW very swiftly grew to dominate the night campaign against Germany mounted by RAF Bomber Command in World War II. Today, the RAF has fought against financial problems to try to climb back to somewhere near the same relative level of capability, although air forces all over the world know the importance of EW and the impossibility of winning without it.

Special sections in this book

describe current EW aircraft, and various forms of EW are the concern of the TR-1, which is dealt with in the first section entitled Reconnaissance Aircraft. It is put here because it is a recent derivative of the U-2, one of the most notorious aircraft in history. It was the first aircraft to be designed specifically for clandestine reconnaissance by illegal overflights, in other words by boldly flying across foreign territory without permission in order to take photographs of military or strategically interesting installations. By 1960 such aircraft were no longer a valid proposition, because of the development of SAMs (surface-to-air missiles) able to reach far higher than aeroplanes can fly. The U-2 was, however, followed by a second-generation reconnaissance aircraft able to fly not only as high but about five times faster, but this extremely costly machine today operates rather infrequently and would probably not penetrate defended airspace. It is generally felt that strategic reconnaissance is best left to the spacecraft, and this is a subject not covered in the present work (although it is dealt with very fully in another Salamander book, *The Intelligence War*, first published in 1983).

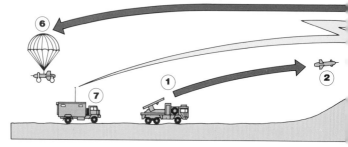

▶ While manned aircraft of many types and diverse size and appearance all make their contribution to the basic tasks of gathering intelligence, keeping ahead in the EW game (and let us keep it a game, with good-natured greetings exchanged by NATO and Soviet crews engaged in the same business), and the equally important business of Command and Control of friendly forces, a further new species of aircraft has lately joined the ranks of the intelligence gatherers, mainly over limited radii and normally over land battles. These are the RPVs.

Small pilotless aircraft were built in large numbers as long ago as 1917, but in order to carry explosives to the enemy by one means or another. Radio-controlled target aeroplanes were common in the 1920s, but it is rather remarkable that no similar machines were used in World War II for reconnaissance. By the end of the 1960s there were many RPVs (remotely piloted vehicles) flying reconnaissance missions, with many kinds of control and many kinds of sensors, and companies in the USA, France, Italy and other countries have all claimed credit for their invention. Briefly, the idea is that cameras or other reconnaissance devices are installed in an aeroplane so small that it could almost be called a model. This is then flown over an enemy target under the control either of a computer or of a pilot back at base or riding in a "mother aircraft" or "drone director" out of harm's way.

Such small and agile machines are surprisingly difficult to shoot down, and compared with manned aircraft their cost is minimal. The clever ones can send back information and pictures by a secure radio link, so it is not a very great loss if the vehicle itself fails to return. This sounds like a civilized way of waging war—at a distance, and without exposing humans to danger.

Left: Nations all over the world are busy with RPV programmes, to some degree because they are fun things which can be flown for a low budget. This is a tail-on view of South Africa's Eyrie, which has a 30hp engine and can fly for five hours at 15,000ft (4.57km). The big funding is needed when the military aspects and sensors get serious.

Below: Possibly the most important of the world's many low-level reconnaissance RPV (drone) systems is the AN/USD-502. This high-speed RPV is carried on a 4-ton truck (1) from which it is launched by a tandem boost rocket. It follows a pre-programmed flight path (2), with its sensors switched on at timed moments (3) over hostile areas. The IRLS (4) sends back signals in real time so that the linescan pictures appear back at truck (7). Thus information is gathered even if the RPV is shot down. If it survives, and it has a better chance than a manned aircraft, it heads for home (5) and recovers by deploying a parachute and rapid-inflating air bags (6) to cushion its descent and avoid unserviceability.

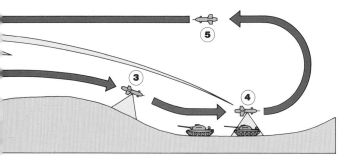

Below: What manned aircraft might be used for tomorrow's reconnaissance missions? Lockheed have published this suggestion for a "super SR-71", but such aircraft would be astronomically expensive and be shot down with ease by modern missiles despite flying at a proposed Mach 5 (3,300mph, 5,311km/h) at 98,427ft.

# Reconnaissance Aircraft

The fact that the RAF no longer has any dedicated reconnaissance aircraft could lead a British observer to the erroneous conclusion that such aircraft are a dying species. Certainly it is tempting just to hang a pod full of sensors under a fighter or attack aircraft, but this is an answer only for those crippled by cutbacks in defence budgets.

At the same time, installing equipment valued at anything upwards of $10 million in an unarmed aircraft flying in harm's way is at best a calculated risk. Can an RF-4E survive flying at 575mph at 500 feet? Can a TR-1 survive flying at 400mph at 85,000 feet? Can an SR-71 or MiG-25 survive flying at 2,000mph at the same great height? The low-flier surely has to rely to a considerable extent on giving the defences inadequate time to react; other aircraft have to rely 100 per cent on their ability to defeat every anti-aircraft defence system and weapon that relies on EM (electromagnetic) radiation, such as radio or radar waves, or IR (infra-red, heat).

Defeating these devices involves either keeping as quiet as possible, by refraining from the emission of any EM radiation, or carrying clever ECM and IRCM countermeasures which throw the hostile devices off the scent. Keeping quiet is impossible, because unless an aircraft shuts down its engine(s) and glides it is bound to emit strong IR radiation from the jet nozzle(s). The reconnaissance devices themselves can be purely passive (non-emitting), relying instead on recording the radiation received from the targets. A special form of reconnaissance, Elint (electronic intelligence), is discussed in the next section. But though so-called "stealth" techniques aim eventually to create aircraft almost invisible to radar, it does not appear possible to devise a militarily useful aircraft that cannot be seen.

Back in 1933 a Soviet team tried to modify a light aircraft until it was as invisible as possible, but found that the engine, crew, fuel, wheels and many detail parts looked more obvious than ever; apart from this, the structural problems gravely reduced the utility of the modified "transparent" aircraft. Today the same problems are being encountered not only at optical wavelengths but also with radars, IR and other parts of the EM spectrum. At the same time, of course, the targets being investigated are likely to be making their own best attempts to merge into the background or to hide behind various forms of camouflage.

Once a simple matter of climbing into the cockpit with a camera and note-pad, aerial reconnaissance today involves such devices as SARs, acoubuoys, magnetometers and reprogrammable computers, as well as the now traditional cameras, IR linescan and Elint recorders. A selection of these are described on the following pages. Of course, as noted earlier, reconnaissance of various kinds is also an important task of military satellites, but these are discussed in a special chapter of another Salamander book, *The Intelligence War*.

What kind of aircraft fly reconnaissance missions? In World War I they were hardly distinguishable from two-seat fighters and light bombers. In World War II almost all reconnaissance aircraft were special versions of high-speed fighters and bombers. In the 1950s many were extremely large machines, such as the RB-36 and RB-52, and even today many of the Soviet Union's reconnaissance missions—in which Elint type operations figure very prominently—are flown by extremely

**Above: Northrop's RF-5E Tigereye is the cheapest of all available high-speed manned reconnaissance aircraft. Its specially designed nose can accommodate a variety of modern sensor systems.**

large aircraft such as the 200-ton Tu-95 and Tu-142 Bear. Such aircraft would almost certainly not be survivable in wartime. The development of truly effective SAM systems has profoundly changed all kinds of combat aircraft, especially those used for reconnaissance.

By far the greatest number of today's reconnaissance aircraft are basically well-known fighter or attack machines either carrying an external pod or modified with internal sensor and dispenser systems which often eliminate the capability of carrying weapons. In most cases their performance is identical to that of the armed version. The sensor fit is always tailored to maximum speed at low level, the regime in which today's aircraft are considered to have the best chance of survival.

Two extremely interesting aircraft have been produced— at very great cost, in major programmes— by Lockheed-California Company. The SR-71 Blackbird and the U-2/TR-1 family are both dedicated reconnaissance platforms capable of no other purpose. One flies very high

and very fast and the other flies very high at a speed today regarded as pedestrian. Height, even greater than 80,000 ft (24.4 km), offers little protection, and high speed can almost be an advantage in preventing evasive manoeuvres. So these aircraft, and the MiG-25R of the Soviet Union, must rely entirely upon their own electronic defence systems to give a high degree of immunity to hostile action.

The extent to which any large aircraft can actually survive in modern defended airspace is a matter for profound and often heated argument. Designers and operators of modern SAM systems would not agree; in their view the target aircraft would have no chance whatsoever. Unarmed recon aircraft pilots feel especially vulnerable, and the world has yet to be told how it is that large budgets continue to be devoted to aircraft such as the TR-1.

In the past 30 years much attention has been paid to seeing what can be done by taking the human pilot out of the aircraft and putting him in a safer place.

# Dassault Mirage III

## Mirage IIIR, IIIRD, IIIR2Z, 5R

**Origin:** Avions Marcel Dassault-Breguet Aviation, Vaucresson, France.
**Type:** Single-seat tactical reconnaissance aircraft.
**Powerplant:** One 13,670lb (6,200kg) thrust SNECMA Atar 9C after-burning turbojet; (R2Z only) one 15,873lb (7,200kg) Atar 9K-50.
**Dimensions:** Span 26ft 11½in (8.22m); length 50ft 10¼in (15.5m); height 14ft 9in (4.5m); wing area 376.7 sq ft (35m²).
**Weights:** Empty (basic R) 14,550lb (6,600kg); maximum take-off 30,200lb (13,700kg).
**Performance:** Maximum speed (clean) 1,450mph (2,335km/h, Mach 2.2) at high altitude; take-off distance (max weight) 5,250ft (1,600m); combat radius (two tanks, hi-lo-hi) 745 miles (1,200km).
**Armament:** Removable belly pack containing two 30mm DEFA 552 guns each with 125 rounds; provision for Mirage III external ordnance loads but not utilised in service.
**History:** Derived from Mirage IIIE, though prototype was converted from short-fuselage IIIA and first flown as IIIR-01 31 October 1961; first production IIIR flown 1 February 1963.
**Users:** France (IIIR, RD); South Africa (IIIRZ, R2Z); Pakistan (IIIRP); Switzerland (IIIRS); Abu Dhabi, Belgium, Colombia, Egypt, Libya (5R versions).

**Below: This was the
original Mirage IIIR, which was
later delivered to the Armée
de l'Air's 33e Escadre de Reconnaissance at Strasbourg. It was
one of the first Mirages to be
delivered with the Atar 9C
engine with a multi-petal vari-
able nozzle giving additional
reheat thrust.**

**Right: Switzerland was a later
customer of Dassault for the
Mirage IIIR, though—as in the
case of the fighter version—the
Swiss IIIRs had a number of
highly non-standard features.
Doppler was not fitted, and
the three external stores visible
in this photograph are all long-
range drop tanks.**

The Mirage IIIR was designed as a dedicated reconnaissance aircraft to replace the RF-84F in the three squadrons of the Armée de l'Air 33e Escadre de Reconnaissance at Strasbourg; 3/33 began conversion in 1963 and 2/33 in 1964, but 1/33 did not convert until 1966. As in most reconnaissance conversions, the differences were centred in the nose, which was made slimmer by removing the Cyrano radar and replacing it with up to five Omera Type 31 optical cameras focused in four arrangements for low-, medium- or high-altitude work and for night reconnaissance, using an automatic flare launcher and photocell to trigger the camera shutters. A Thomson-CSF radar altimeter automatically adjusts frame repetition rate in relation to ground speed and altitude. The IIIRD and Pakistani RP have a chin bulge for doppler radar, a gyro sight and a modified nose pack containing Omera Types 40 and 33 cameras. The 5R is a similar conversion of the Mirage 5, sold to customers already buying that aircraft. Since 1971 most customers have added SAT Cyclope 160.A5 IR linescan in a modified nose installation.

# Dassault Mirage IV

## Mirage IVR

**Origin:** Avions Marcel Dassault-Breguet Aviation, Vaucresson, France.
**Type:** Limited-range strategic reconnaissance aircraft.
**Powerplant:** Two 15,432lb (7,000kg) thrust (maximum afterburner) SNECMA Atar 9K single-shaft augmented turbojets.
**Dimensions:** Span 38ft 10½in (11.85m); length 77ft 1in (23.5m); height 17ft 8½in (5.4m).
**Weights:** Empty about 33,000lb (15,000kg); loaded 73,800lb (33,475kg).
**Performance:** Maximum speed (dash) 1,454mph (2,340km/h, Mach 2.2) at 40,000ft (13.12km), (sustained) 1,222mph (1,966km/h, Mach 1.7) at 60,000ft (19.68km); time to climb to 36,090ft (11km), 4mins 15secs; service ceiling 65,620ft (20km); tactical radius (dash to target, hi-subsonic return) 770 miles (1,240km); ferry range 2,485 miles (4,000km).
**Armament:** None.
**History:** First flight (IV) 17 June 1959.
**Users:** France (Armée de l'Air).

When the French government decided in 1954 to create a national nuclear deterrent force, the most obvious problem was to choose a delivery system for the bombs. The likely enemy appeared to be the Soviet Union and this involved a long mission flown at high speed. After studying developments of the Vautour—a type used to form the nucleus of the *Force de Frappe*—Dassault began work on a bomber derived from a 1956 project for a twin-engined night fighter. After a year the design had to be scaled up to be powered by two Pratt & Whitney J75B engines, to meet more severe

demands on speed, load and the range sufficient to reach desirable targets and then fly to places outside the Soviet Union. The final choice was to adopt extensive inflight refuelling, which allowed the design to shrink again to an intermediate level. As a result the force of 62 bombers that was eventually created relied totally upon Boeing KC-135F tankers, with booms fitted for probe/drogue refuelling, and also upon the ''buddy technique'' whereby aircraft would fly a mission in pairs, one carrying a bomb and the other spare fuel and a refuelling hose-reel for transfer to its partner. Even so, the initial planning of the Commandement des Forces Aériennes Stratégique presupposed that most missions would be one-way (or at least would not return to France). Dispersal was maximised, with the force divided into three Escadres (91 at Mont de Marsan, 93 at Istres and 94 at Avord), which in turn were subdivided into three four-aircraft groups, two of which were always dispersed away from Escadrille HQ. Despite being a heavy and ''hot'' aircraft, the IVA has also been rocket-blasted out of short unpaved strips hardened by quick setting chemicals sprayed on the soil.

Of the original total of 62 Mirage IVs, only 36 are currently at readiness in the bomber role, but another 12 have been largely rebuilt as dedicated reconnaissance aircraft, designated IVR. Losing their ability to carry a nuclear store, they have large, classified installations which include optical cameras, an IR linescan and, it is believed, a SLAR (Side-Looking Airborne Radar), all installed in the underside of the fuselage. There is a possibility that an SAR (Synthetic-Aperture Radar) may become available, although none is known to exist in France. Dassault state that they did not carry out the IVR conversions.

**Below: Seen here at the Tours air base of l'Armée de l'Air on 13 November 1981, the IVR normally carries a large multisensor pod filling the weapon bay and projecting in a fairing over the camera and IRLS windows. Mapping radar is retained.**

# Dassault Mirage F1

## Mirage F1.CR

**Origin:** Avions Marcel Dassault-Breguet Aviation, Vaucresson, France.
**Type:** Single-seat tactical reconnaissance aircraft.
**Powerplant:** One 15,873lb (7,200kg) thrust SNECMA Atar 9K-50 afterburning turbojet.
**Dimensions:** Span 27ft 6¾in (8.4m); length 49ft 2½in (15m); height 14ft 9in (4.5m); wing area 269.1 sq ft (25m²).
**Weights:** Empty 16,600lb (7,530kg); maximum take-off 35,715lb (16,200kg).
**Performance:** Maximum speed (clean) 1,450mph (2,335km/h, Mach 2.2) at high altitude; take-off distance (F1.C on interception mission) 2,100ft (640m); combat radius (hi-lo-hi) 620 miles (1,000km).
**Armament:** Two 30mm DEFA 553 guns each with 125 rounds; external weapons normally not carried.
**History:** Derived from F1 fighter first flown 23 December 1966; first F1.CR (converted from F1.C-200 fighter) flown 20 November 1981.
**Users:** France (Armée de l'Air).

As a replacement in the Armée de l'Air for the delta-winged Mirage IIIR/RD aircraft, which for almost 20 years has equipped the three squadrons of the 33e Escadre de Reconnaissance at Strasbourg, the Mirage F1.CR has been produced by the same kind of modification that had previously led to the IIIR and the doppler-equipped RD. The basis is the F1.C-200. The F1.C was the original Armée de l'Air production fighter, which was first delivered in March 1973. Compared with the delta Mirage III and 5 it has a much smaller but far more efficient wing, separate horizontal tail (allowing high-lift flaps and drooping leading edge), much greater internal fuel capacity and twin-wheel landing gears. The Dash-200 version has a fixed, permanently

**Above: The 33e Escadre at Strasbourg has been converting from the delta Mirage IIIR to today's far superior Mirage F1.CR. All CR aircraft carry the fixed inflight-refuelling probe.**

attached inflight-refuelling probe. One of these aircraft was converted into the prototype CR following the original decision in February 1979. Reconnaissance equipment includes an Omera 35 oblique frame camera, an Omera 40 panoramic camera and an IR sensor, as well as a sight recorder. An external pod will house further optical and EM sensors, probably including IR linescan. New equipment includes an ESD navigational radar (derived from Cyrano IV) in the nose and a SAGEM inertial navigation system. Aircraft for the inventory are finished in low-visibility grey. Including two prototypes, the Armée de l'Air order amounts to 64 machines, and the first of the 33e wing's squadrons was due to convert before the end of 1983.

**Below: The first Mirage F1.CR, before it was painted in camouflage.**

# Grumman OV-1 Mohawk

## OV-1D, RV-1D

**Origin:** Grumman Aerospace, Bethpage, NY, USA.
**Type:** Two-seat multisensor reconnaissance observation aircraft.
**Powerplant:** Two 1,160shp Lycoming T53-701 turboprops.
**Dimensions:** Span (A, C) 42ft (12.8m); (D) 48ft (14.63m); length 41ft (12.5m); (D with SLAR, 44ft 11in, 13.69m); height 12ft 8in (3.86m).
**Weights:** Empty (A) 9,937lb (4,507kg); (B) 11,067lb (5,020kg); (C) 10,400lb (4,717kg); (D) 12,054lb (5,467kg); maximum loaded (A) 15,031lb (6,818kg); (B, C) 19,230lb (8,722kg); (D) 18,109lb (8,214kg).
**Performance:** Maximum speed (all variants) 297-310mph (480-500km/h); initial climb (A) 2,950ft (0.9km)/min, (B) 2,250ft (0.716km)/min, (C) 2,670ft (0.814km)/min, (D) 3,618ft (1.1km)/min; service ceiling (all) 28,000-31,000ft (8.5-9.4km); range with external fuel (A) 1,410 miles (2,270km); (B) 1,230 miles (1,980km); (C) 1,330 miles (2,140km); (D) 1,011 miles (1,627km).
**Armament:** Not normally fitted, but can include a wide variety of air-to-ground weapons including grenade launchers, Minigun pods and small guided missiles.

Above: Grumman's G-134 Mohawk represents the only important member of an inter-mediate class of reconnaissance aircraft, bigger and more powerful than light aircraft yet slower than the jets. It was planned in the 1950s when survival over the battlefield was a much simpler business than it is today.

Right: This specially equipped OV-1 Mohawk was photographed on daring missions close to the erupting volcano Mount St Helens, Washington, in 1981. It was using its SLAR and IR linescan, as well as other instrumentation, to try to assist predictions of the volcano's future activity—an unusual recon mission.

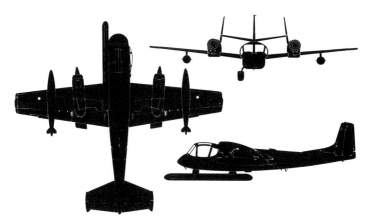

**Above: Grumman OV-1D with SLAR and underwing drop tanks.**

**History:** First flight (YOV-1A) 14 April 1959; service delivery February 1961; final delivery (new aircraft) December 1970.
**Users:** USA (Army), Israel, Pakistan.

Developed in the late 1950s to meet a cogently argued need by the US Army (at first supported by the Marine Corps), the OV-1 is in some ways unique. A STOL fixed-wing machine, it has a quite low performance, but it is agile, well equipped with all-weather navigation, communications and reconnaissance systems, and as far as possible protected against ground fire. The pilot on the left and observer or sensor operator on the right sit in Martin-Baker ejection seats and have a commanding field of view except to the rear. The standard current model is the OV-1D which apart from optical cameras and, in some cases, Elint receivers, can be quickly converted to carry either UAS-4 IR linescan surveillance equipment or an APS-94 SLAR (Side-Looking Aircraft Radar) slung externally under the fuselage. The US Army is maintaining a force of 110, plus 36 RV-1Ds equipped solely for Elint missions. Israel has four OV-1Ds with local modifications. In mid-1983 a number of OV-1Ds were being refurbished for supply to Pakistan for surveillance along the frontier with India. They have new cameras, IRLS and SLAR for surveillance up to 93 miles (150km) into India.

# Lockheed SR-71

## SR-71A, B, C

**Origin:** Lockheed-California Co, Burbank, California, USA.
**Type:** (A) strategic reconnaissance aircraft; (B,C) trainer.
**Powerplant:** Two 32,500lb (14,742kg) thrust Pratt & Whitney J58-1 (JT11D-20B) continuous-bleed afterburning turbojets.
**Dimensions:** Span 55ft 7in (16.94m); length 107ft 5in (32.74m); height 18ft 6in (5.64m); wing area 1,800 sq ft (167.2m²).
**Weights:** Empty not disclosed, but about 65,000lb (29,500kg); loaded 170,000lb (77,112kg).
**Performance:** Maximum speed (also maximum cruising speed) about 2,100mph (3,380km/h) at over 60,000ft (18.29km), world record speed over 15-mile (25km) course 2,193mph (3,530km/h, Mach 3.31); maximum sustained height (also world record) 85,069ft (25.9km); range at 78,740ft (24km) at 1,983mph (3,191km/h, Mach 3) on internal fuel 2,982 miles (4,800km); corresponding endurance 1hr 30mins; endurance at loiter speed up to 7hrs.
**Armament:** None.
**History:** First flight (A-11) 26 April 1962, (SR) 22 December 1964.
**Users:** USA (Air Force).

Unbelievably, Lockheed and the Air Force succeeded in designing, building and completing the flight-test programme of these extremely large and noisy aircraft in total secrecy. President Johnson disclosed the existence of the basic A-11 design in February 1964. It was created by Lockheed's Advanced Development Projects team — the so-called Skunk Works — under vice-president C.L. "Kelly" Johnson in 1959–61. The requirement was for a platform able to succeed the U-2 for clandestine reconnaissance, and as height was no longer sufficient protection, speed had to be added (which in ▶

**Below: Parked in a readiness shelter, this SR-71A has its all-moving rudders, called "verticals", displaced from the neutral position.**

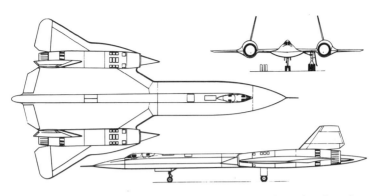

Above: Three-view of the SR-71A with spikes out and nozzles closed.

Above: The unfamiliar flat underside and sharp chines of the SR-71 are the inevitable result of having to cruise at over 2,000mph.

**Above:** You do not just decide to fly an SR-71 and walk out to it. Preparations resemble a space mission, and here Maj Cliff Cunningham, training chief of the 9th SRW's Personnel Service Division, demonstrates the vital life-support system.

**Right:** An SR-71A taxis in at Beale led by a Follow Me truck, its braking parachute doors still open above the fuselage. This head-on view shows the way the giant inlet spikes (still far too hot to touch) are canted downwards and inwards.

**Below:** The penultimate SR-71A about to touch down, with engines idling and the drag chute about to deploy.

►turn translated into still greater height). Unprecedented engineering problems were encountered with the airframe (made principally from titanium and its alloys, never before used for primary structure), the propulsion system (which at cruising speed glows orange-white at the nozzles yet gets most of its thrust from the inlets) and even the hydraulic system (which uses completely new materials and techniques). Basic features included a modified delta wing with a pronounced camber on the outer leading edges, extremely large lifting strakes extended forwards along the body and nacelles, twin inward-canted pivoted fins above the nacelles, outboard ailerons, inboard elevators and main gears with three wheels side-by-side. The original A-11 shape also featured fixed ventral fins under the rear of the nacelles and a larger hinged central ventral fin which folded upwards to enable the aircraft to land.

The first three aircraft (60-6934/6) were built as YF-12A research interceptors, with a pressurised cockpit for a pilot and an air interception officer, Hughes ASG-18 pulse-doppler radar, side chines cut back to avoid the radome and provide lateral locations for two IR seekers, and tandem missile bays for (usually) eight AIM-47 AAMs. In 1969-72 two participated in a joint programme with NASA to investigate many aspects of flight at around Mach 3. These aircraft investigated surface finishes other than the ►

**Above: At least four different tail badges have been worn by SR-71As, all of them only semi-official. The most famous is the snake emblem denoting service over south-east Asia during the Vietnam war. This aircraft sports the Bunny badge which has been painted on hundreds of aircraft of all the US armed services. This photograph was taken over the Sierra Nevada.**

**Right: After a mission the SR-71A flight crew, in their brown pressure suits with special life-support systems, complete various checks and vital actions before disembarking via a large stairway, accompanied by specialist ground personnel. Four ground crew with hand-cranks open up the scaldingly hot inlet-duct doors to begin inspection. Lockheed is now working on the Covert Survivable In-weather Recon/ Strike (CSIRS) aircraft, using stealth techniques, of which the USAF hopes to be able to deploy 20. If CSIRS is built it will gradually replace the SR-71A as the USA's global manned surveillance platform.**

▶ normal bluish-black which resulted in the popular name of ''Blackbird'' for all aircraft of this family, and at least one was experimentally fitted with canard foreplanes for the flight programme.

It is believed that about 15 aircraft were delivered to the Air Force with a generally similar standard of build, though configured for the reconnaissance/strike role. Designated A-11, they could carry a centreline pod

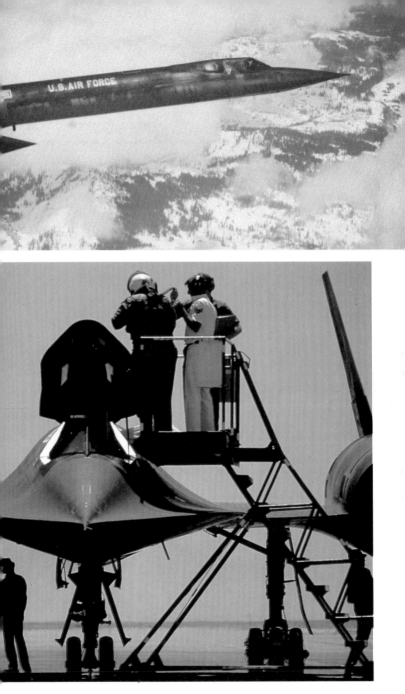

which could be a 1-megaton bomb but was usually a GTD-21 reconnaissance drone looking like a scaled-down single engined A-11 and with cameras, IR and (variously, according to mission) other sensors in a bay behind the multishock centrebody nose inlet. Some dozens of these RPVs were delivered, painted the same heat-reflective black and with similar flight performance (engine has not been disclosed) but with rather shorter ▶

**Above: An unusual view of an SR-71A as it returns to Beale AFB, California.**

**Below: Another landing picture, this time showing the drag-chute streamed by an SR-71B.**

**Below: Preceded by a convoy of cars, this SR-71A is taxiing out.**

► endurance. Those not consumed in missions (about 17) were stored at Davis-Monthan.

The A-11/GTD-21 held the fort until, in 1964, the definitive long-range recon/strike RS-71A came into service. (It was announced by President Johnson as the SR-71A and as he was never corrected the "SR" designation became accepted.) This also can carry a 1-MT bomb pod or GTD-21 or derived RPV, but details of missions and payloads have not been disclosed. With an airframe and increased-capacity fuel system first flown on the fourth A-11 (designated YF-12C), it is longer and has ►

**Above: The crew of an SR-71A leaving their aircraft, helmets off, after a mission in early 1982.**

**Below: Opening up inspection panels following an SR-71A reconnaissance mission.**

▶optimized forward chines extending to the tip of the nose; it has no rear ventrals nor a missile bay, but extremely comprehensive and in some cases unique reconnaissance systems for the surveillance of from 60,000 to 80,000 square miles (155,000 to 207,000km²) per hour are fitted. The back-seater, with a separate clamshell canopy with inserted panes of heat-resistant glass, is the reconnaissance systems officer (RSO). Both crew wear astronaut suits and follow pre-flight procedures based on those of space missions.

The first SR-71A was assigned to a new unit, the 4200th SRW, at Beale AFB, California, in 1966, which worked up the optimum operating procedures and techniques for best coverage, optimum fuel consumption, minimal signatures and precision navigation, burning special JP-7 fuel topped up in flight by KC-135Q tankers also based at Beale. To facilitate the demanding process of crew conversion to this extremely costly aircraft, an operational trainer, the SR-71B, was purchased, at least two being slotted into the main batch of 29 (or more) which began at 61-7950. This has a raised instructor cockpit and dual pilot controls, and also includes the reconnaissance systems for RSO training.

After the first crew had qualified as fully operational, in 1971, the parent wing was restyled the 9th SRW, with two squadrons. This has since operated in a clandestine manner, rarely more than two aircraft being despatched to any overseas theatre and missions normally being flown by single aircraft. It is not known to what extent subsonic cruise is used; in the normal high-speed regime the skin temperature rises from −49°C to 550-595°C, and the fuel serves as the heat sink and rises to a temperature of about 320°C before reaching the engines. At least one SR-71C was produced as an SR-71A rebuild, following the loss of an SR-71B. It has been estimated that the SR-71As seldom fly more than 200hrs per year, mainly on training exercises. No recent estimate has been published of their vulnerability.

**Below: One of the first air-to-air photographs ever taken of an SR-71A, showing the first of the 31 ordered on an early test flight. In peacetime these impressive machines have proved of very great value, but their ability to survive in war is problematical. Stealth techniques are now recognised as more important than performance.**

# Lockheed U-2/TR-1

## U-2A, B, C, CT, D, R, WU-2 family, TR-1A, B

**Origin:** Lockheed-California Co, Burbank, California, USA.

**Type:** High-altitude photo-reconnaissance, multisensor reconnaissance and special reconnaissance aircraft; (CT) dual trainer; (WU) weather research aircraft.

**Powerplant:** One Pratt & Whitney unaugmented turbojet (A and some derivatives) 11,200lb (5,080kg) thrust J57-13A or -37A, (most other U-2 versions) one 17,000lb (7,711kg) thrust J75-13, (TR-1) 17,000lb (7,711kg) J75-13B.

**Dimensions:** Span (A, B, C, CT, D) 80ft (24.38m), (R, WU-2C, TR-1) 103ft (31.89m); length (typical of early versions) 49ft 7in (15.1m), (R, TR) 63ft (19.2m); wing area (early) 565 sq ft (52.49m²), (R, TR) 1,000 sq ft (92.9m²).

**Weights:** Empty (A) 9,920lb (4,500kg), (B,C,CT,D) typically 11,700lb (5,350kg), (R) 14,990lb (6,800kg), (TR) about 16,000lb (7,258kg); loaded (A) 14,800lb (6,713kg), (B, C, CT, D, clean) typically 16,000lb (7,258kg), (with 89 US gal wing tanks) 17,270lb (7,833kg), (R) 29,000lb (13,154kg), (TR) 40,000lb (18,144kg).

**Performance:** Maximum speed (A) 494mph (795km/h), (B,C,CT,D) 528mph (850km/h), (R) about 510mph (821km/h), (TR) probably about 495mph (797km/h); maximum cruising speed (most) 460mph (740km/h), (TR) 430mph (692km/h); operational ceiling (A) 70,000ft (21.34km), (B,C,CT,D) 85,000ft (25.9km), (R,TR) about 90,000ft (27.43km); maximum range (A) 2,200 miles (3,540km), (B,C,CT,D) 3,000 miles (4,830km), (R) about 3,500 miles (5,833km), (TR) about 4,000 miles (6,437km); endurance on internal fuel (A) 5½hrs, (B,C,CT,D) 6½hrs, (R) 7½hrs, (TR) 12hrs.

**Armament:** None.

**History:** First flight (U-2) 1 August 1955, (TR-1A) September 1981.

**Users:** USA (Air Force); also used by NASA.

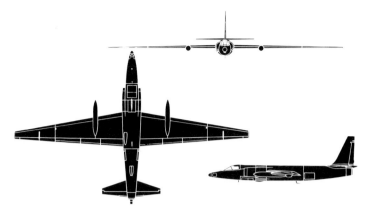

**Above: Three-view of the original U-2B, similar to that shot down on 1 May 1960. This was a much lighter aircraft than the giant TR-1.**

First of the two families of clandestine surveillance aircraft produced by Lockheed's "Skunk Works" under the brilliant engineering leadership of C.L. "Kelly" Johnson, the U-2 was conceived in spring 1954 to meet an unannounced joint USAF/CIA requirement for a reconnaissance and research aircraft to cruise at the highest attainable altitudes. The entire programme was cloaked in secrecy, test flying (under Tony LeVier) took place at remote Watertown Strip, Nevada, and no announcement was made of delivery to the Air Force of 56-675 and 676, the two prototypes. The original order comprised 48 single-seaters and five tandem-seat aircraft, the back-seater initially being an observer or systems operator. The operating unit was styled Weather Reconnaissance Squadron, Provisional (1st), and soon moved to Atsugi AB, Japan, while the WRS,P (2nd), moved to Wiesbaden, Germany, with basing also at Lakenheath, England. The WRS,P (3rd), remained at Edwards to develop techniques and handle research. ▶

**Above: Described in another Salamander book, *Modern Military Aircraft,* the EPX was a US Navy version with special overwater radar, the Texas Instruments APS-116 (Mod) as used on the S-3.**

**Left: Various U-2s operated from British bases right up to the TR-1s of today. This U-2R of the USAF 349th Strategic Reconnaissance Squadron was seen leaving RAF Wethersfield in July 1975.**

▶  Intense interest in the aircraft, grey and without markings, prompted an announcement that they were NASA research machines with the "Utility" designation U-2, but after numerous unmolested missions over the Soviet Union, China and other territories, one of the CIA aircraft was shot down near Sverdlovsk on 1 May 1960. Subsequent missions were flown by USAF pilots in uniform, with USAF markings on the aircraft. Several more J75-powered aircraft were shot down over China and Cuba, and attrition was also fairly high from accidents, because the U-2 is possibly the most difficult of all modern aircraft to fly. Features include an all-metal airframe of sailplane-like qualities, with a lightly loaded and extremely flexible wing, tandem bicycle landing gears, outrigger twin-wheel units jettisoned on take-off (the landing tipping on to a downturned wingtip), an unpressurised cockpit with a UV-protected sliding canopy of F-104 type, special low-volatility fuel, and large flaps, airbrakes and braking parachute.

From 1959 the J75 engine was installed, and with the U-2C the inlets were splayed out at the front, the U-2D being the original two-seat version ▶

**Above left: This aircraft, the last but one of the U-2B batch, was modified six times and is seen as an air-sampling JU-2D in 1970.**

**Left: Later the same aircraft was rebuilt as a U-2D two-seater, one of an important sub-family used by the USAF Flight Test Center.**

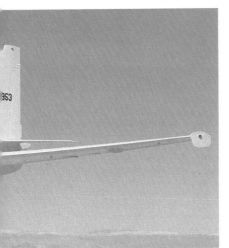

Left: As the U-2 was extremely difficult to fly Lockheed built the dual-control U-2CT trainer. At one time the much-rebuilt 56-6721 (above) was a U-2CT. This photograph shows another example, 56-6953.

Below: Much bigger and almost three times as heavy as the first U-2s, today's TR-1s are extremely costly high-altitude surveillance platforms to be used around potentially hostile frontiers. This TR-1A is about to have its out-rigger wheels replaced.

Above: The eleventh U-2R, 68-10339, flying in clean condition without wing pods. Note how the bulged inlets, first seen on the U-2C, give a silhouette outline resembling the U-2CT trainer; note also the elevated platform carrying the tail, with no dorsal spine.

Right: The U-2R, illustrated, looks almost identical to the TR-1, though the latter is much heavier and costs more than twice as much. Low wing-loading, a mere 29lb/sq ft (141kg/m²) in the standard U-2R at gross weight, is the key to the ability of these odd sailplane-like machines to fly at heights up to 90,000ft (27.43km).

Below: This machine, built as a USAF U-2B, was later re-registered as a legitimate civil research aircraft, with ejection seat and small doghouse blister. Photograph taken at Palmdale in about 1960.

►and the U-2CT (conversion trainer) being one of at least six rebuilds, in this example as a dual-control pilot trainer with the instructor seated at an upper level. Most CTs have been stationed at the Air Force Flight Test Center and Test Pilot School, both at Edwards. The AFFTC also uses several other versions, including D variants with special instrumentation, dorsal or ventral inlets for sampling, and various external payloads, with a variety of black, white and other paint schemes. Both C and D models have large dorsal "doghouse" fairings for sampling, sensing or avionic equipment.

Because of high attrition the line was reopened in 1968 for 12 considerably larger aircraft styled U-2R (68-10329 to 10340). While

most earlier models could carry 80 US gal (336l) tanks on the leading edge, the R was supplied with large wing pods permanently installed and accommodating various payloads as well as 105 US gal (398l) fuel. Wet wings increased internal capacity, and the R also introduced a stretched airframe able to accommodate all necessary fuel and equipment internally. Front and rear main gears were moved closer together, and the rear fuselage was formed into a bulged upper platform carrying the tailplane. All known U-2R aircraft have been matt black, serving with various overseas commands. ►

▶ The latest variant, the TR-1, is basically a further updated U-2R with ASARS (Advanced Synthetic-Aperture Radar System), in the form of the UPD-X side-looking airborne radar, and with dramatically increased integral-tank fuel capacity, which results in very much higher gross weight. A single-seater (like the R), the TR-1A carries extensive new avionics in its pods; as well as much more comprehensive ECM; mission equipment is also carried in the nose, in the Q-bay behind the cockpit and between the inlet ducts. Because of the long endurance the astronaut-suited pilot has special facilities for his personal comfort and for taking warm food. The first batch of aircraft comprised two TR-1As (80-1061 and 1062) and a third (1063) which was actually the first to be delivered, on 10 June 1981, via the Air Force to NASA with the designation ER-2 for earth-resource missions. Next followed three more TR-1As and a two-seat TR-1B, the eventual fleet being expected to number 33 As and two Bs. Ten of the single-seaters are to be allocated to the PLSS (Precision Location Strike System) mission for pinpointing and destroying electronic emitters far into hostile territory. Of the remaining 25 aircraft, 18 are to be based at RAF Alconbury, England, where operations began under SAC control in early 1983. Forward operating locations in Germany and elsewhere will extend mission endurance over Warsaw Pact frontiers. What has not yet been explained is how these slow-flying and defenceless aircraft, which obviously do not conform with modern stealth concepts, might survive in any European war. Height alone is no protection, and against the latest Soviet anti-aircraft weapons it would be perilous to rely totally upon friendly jamming platforms such as the EF-111A.

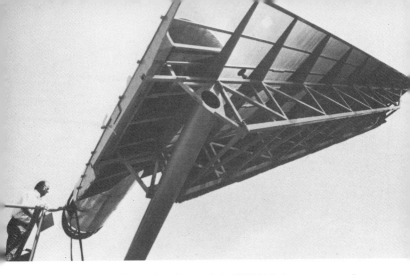

**Above:** In late 1982 Lockheed tested the DME (distance-measuring equipment) of the TR-1 PLSS using a pod on an inverted wing mock-up.

**Below:** USAF 80-1064 was the first two-seat TR-1B. Though a conversion and systems trainer, it is quite different from the U-2CT.

# McDonnell Douglas RF-4 Phantom

## RF-4B, RF-4C, RF-4E, RF-4EJ

**Origin:** McDonnell Aircraft Company, St Louis, Missouri, USA.
**Type:** High-speed low-level multisensor reconnaissance aircraft.
**Powerplant:** (B) two 17,000lb (7,711kg) thrust General Electric J79-8B afterburning turbojets; (C) 17,000lb (7,711kg) J79-15; (E, EJ) 17,900lb (8,120kg) J79-17.
**Dimensions:** Span 38ft 5in (11.7m); length (B,C) 62ft 10½in (19.19m), (E) 63ft (19.2m); height 16ft 5in (5m); wing area 530 sq ft (49.2m²).
**Weights:** Empty (B) 29,300lb (13,290kg), (C) 28,292lb (12,833kg, (E, EJ) typically 30,400lb (13,789kg); basic mission take-off gross weight (C) 42,689lb (19,364kg); maximum (B, C) 58,000lb (26,300kg), (E, EJ) up to about 61,000lb (27,670kg).
**Performance:** Maximum speed (clean) 910mph (1,464km/h, Mach 1.19) at sea level, 1,432mph (2,304km/h), Mach 2.17) at high altitude; service ceiling (E) 58,750ft (17.9km); max range on internal fuel 2,300 miles (3,700km); basic mission radius 526 miles (846km); combat radius 971 miles (1,562km).
**Armament:** None.
**History:** First flight (C) 8 August 1963, (B) 12 March 1965, (E) 15 September 1970.
**Users:** (B) USA (Marine Corps); (C) USA (Air Force); (E) West Germany, Israel, Iran, Turkey, Greece, Japan.

▶

**Below: The Federal German Luftwaffe uses a unique recon-naissance model, the RF-4E, based on the advanced F-4E.**

**Right: The RF-4 reconnaissance Phantoms all have a small mapping radar in the nose and a forward oblique chin camera.**

**Below: This aircraft is a regular RF-4C of the USAF, carrying droptanks. Camouflage hides the HF shunt antenna in the fin skin.**

45

▶The most famous fighter in the Western world throughout the 1960s and 1970s, the F-4 Phantom II is so large and capable that it was evident from the start that it would form the basis for an outstanding reconnaissance aircraft. The original customer, the US Navy, chose not to acquire this variant, despite presentations by MAC of dedicated multisensor versions and externally carried pods, but the USAF very quickly contracted for the RF-4C, which set a totally new standard in high-speed fighter-type aircraft used solely for multisensor reconnaissance without armament.

Though having the same internal and external fuel as the fighter versions (external fuel: one 500gal, 2,273l, centreline tank plus two 301gal, 1,368l, wing tanks) and a basically unchanged airframe, the RF-4C introduced a new nose, longer and slimmer, with no main radar but a small APQ-99 forward-looking radar and a main bay occupied by forward oblique, vertical and lateral oblique cameras. In the fuselage is an APQ-102 SLAR and an AAS-18A IR linescan. Various new communications include HF radio with a shunt aerial flush with the skin on each side of the fin. Ahead of the fin are two photoflash installations firing the cartridges upwards.

Development was extremely successful, and 505 examples were delivered to the USAF. The Marines bought 46 RF-4Bs with similar equipment but also including cameras on rotating mountings, aimed by the pilot, and an inertial navigation system. Newest and best of the recon variants is the RF-4E, all built for export. This is based on the F-4E, with more powerful engines, an extra fuel tank in the tail, slatted stabilators (tailplanes) and, in more recent models, automatic manoeuvring slats on the wing in place of blown droop flaps. MCAIR exported 130 but did not assemble the parts for the last 16 (of 32) for Iran.

**Below: Fighter Phantoms can also fly reconnaissance missions with the use of camera or multisensor pods hung externally. This fighter F-4, apparently an F-4J or a related version of the Navy, is equipped with forward and lateral oblique cameras carried in a pod under the left wing, here seen opened for servicing and magazine reloading.**

Above: In its day the RF-4C was the most capable tactical reconnaissance aircraft in the world, combining exceptional range with very high speed, excellent manoeuvrability and a large mission payload. This example serves with the 1st Tac Recon Sqn.

Below: Another view of an RF-4E of the West German Luftwaffe. This model has most of the sensors of the USAF RF-4C and also has an extra (No 7) tank in the rear fuselage, a later nose radar and slightly more powerful J79 engines matched to the increased gross weight. A total of 75 of this version was bought, West German industry participating in the manufacture of the airframes.

# Mikoyan/Guryevich MiG-25

## MiG-25R Foxbat-B, D

**Origin:** The OKB named for Mikoyan and Guryevich, Soviet Union.
**Type:** Single-seat high-altitude reconnaissance aircraft.
**Powerplant:** Two 24,250lb (11,000kg) thrust Tumanskii R-31 afterburning turbojets.
**Dimensions;** Span 44ft (13.4m); length 78ft 1¾in (23.82m); height 20ft 0¼in (6.1m); wing area 603 sq ft (56m²).
**Weights:** Empty (B) 43,200lb (19,600kg); maximum take-off 73,635lb (33,400kg).
**Performance:** Maximum speed (clean) 2,115mph (3,400km/h, Mach 3.2); maximum speed below 10,000ft (3km) Mach 0.8; maximum operating height 88,580ft (27km); operating radius (no external fuel, max cruise power) 680 miles (1,100km).
**Armament:** Normally none; most reconnaissance versions are believed to have no provision for weapons.
**History:** First flight (Ye-266 prototype) prior to April 1965, (MiG-25R prototype) prior to 1969.
**Users:** Soviet Union, Algeria, Egypt, India, Libya, Syria.

Originally designed as a stand-off interceptor to kill high-flying B-70 (RS-70) Valkyrie bombers, the MiG-25 emerged as an aircraft with powerful radar and AAMs and possessed of tremendous speed and climb capability, but with extremely limited power of manoeuvre. At speeds in the region of Mach 3 it flies essentially in a straight line, whilst burning fuel at a prodigious rate. It was an obvious basis for a high-flying ultra-fast reconnaissance aircraft, and the first MiG-25R version was in service with Soviet FA (Frontal Aviation) regiments by 1970.

Compared with the MiG-25 interceptor, the reconnaissance versions have a wing of reduced area, with slightly less span and constant sweep from root to tip. The nose radar is removed, giving a conical nose offering reduced drag; inside this (in the basic version known to NATO as Foxbat-B) are five very large vertical, forward oblique, lateral and panoramic cameras and a SLAR "looking" through a dielectric panel on the left side of the nose. Doppler radar is believed to be fitted, as on many of the interceptor version. Foxbat-D is a less common variant with a much larger SLAR installation and probably IR linescan but no cameras; this is used by the Soviet Union and Libya only. About 160 MiG-25Rs of both models are estimated to be in FA service, plus about 45 with foreign customers.

Above: The willingness of the Soviet planners to accept a different wing for the MiG-25R emphasises the fact that, unlike the West, the Russians are prepared to spend as much as is needed on military hardware. In this view from below camera windows and the left-side SLAR can be seen.

Below: Both known versions of the MiG-25R are seen in this superb photograph, Foxbat-B being nearer the camera and the probably less common Foxbat-D being in the rear on the left. Drop tanks appear to be needed only on rare occasions, despite the high fuel consumption.

# Northrop RF-5

## RF-5E

**Origin:** Northrop Corporation, Hawthorne, California, USA.
**Type:** Single-seat tactical fighter/reconnaissance aircraft.
**Powerplant:** Two 5,000lb (2,268kg) thrust General Electric J85-21B afterburning turbojets.
**Dimensions:** Span (excluding missiles) 26ft 8in (8.13m); length 48ft 0¾in (14.65m); height 13ft 4in (4.06m); wing area 186 sq ft (17.3m$^2$).
**Weights:** Not known.
**Performance:** Maximum speed (clean), 1,077mph (1,734km/h), Mach 1.63) at high altitude; service ceiling 51,000ft (15.5km); mission radius (one tank, hi-lo-hi) 471 miles (759km), (three tanks) 644 miles (1,037km).
**Armament:** Retains essentially the same armament potential as the F-5E, with a Sidewinder AAM on each wingtip, though normally only one M39A2 20mm gun is fitted and external pylons are used only for up to three drop tanks.
**History:** First flight (F-5) 30 July 1959, (F-5E) 11 August 1972, (RF-5E aerodynamic prototype) January 1979, (production) 15 December 1982.
**Users:** (First customers) Malaysia, Saudi Arabia.

Like the entire F-5 programme in all its versions, the RF-5E Tigereye is a company project without funding from the US Government, and aimed entirely at the export market. There was an RF version of the original F-5A, and a conversion of the F-5E Tiger II was natural: it is a very attractive and cost-effective machine. The radar is replaced by a new, longer nose with a different profile in which can be installed a forward oblique KS-87D1 frame camera and any of a growing series of pallets on which are mounted selected sensors. Pallet 1 mounts a KA-95B medium-altitude panoramic camera, KA-56E low-altitude panoramic camera and RS-710E IR linescan. Pallet 2 combines a KA-56E with a KA-93B6 panoramic camera with 145°

**Above: The prototype RF-5E Tigereye was originally test-flown at Edwards in natural metal finish, with US Air Force on the nose (though it has not been bought by that service). The shape of camera-filled nose is seen here; all windows are of optically flat glass.**

**Left: Subsequently the Tigereye prototype was given this camouflage finish and appropriate tail badge. Few aircraft offer such cost/effective reconnaissance over tactical ranges, though today of course the ability of any conventional aircraft to survive is doubtful.**

scan angle for use at heights from 10,000 to 50,000ft (3-15km). Pallet 3 is for Lorop (Long-Range Oblique Photo) missions and has a KS-174A Lorop camera of 66in (1.68m) focal length. Other pallets which might become available include one with a Zeiss mapping camera, two IR linescans and Elint receivers. The pilot has advanced navigation and communications systems, including INS (updatable on overflying a recognised feature) and a TV display for visual correction of photo runs. Within the first three years the prototype had been evaluated by 31 countries, and the order book is growing. Conversions of existing F-5Es would be possible, thus offering economical recon aircraft at low cost.

# Rockwell International OV-10 Bronco

## OV-10A, OV-10C, OV-10D, OV-10E, OV-10F

**Origin:** Rockwell International, North American Aircraft Operations, El Segundo, California, USA.
**Type:** Two-seat light surveillance and Co-In aircraft.
**Powerplant:** Two 715shp Garrett T76-416/417 turboprops; (OV-10D) 1,040shp T76-420/421.
**Dimensions:** Span 40ft (12.19m), (OV-10D) 44ft (13.41m); length 41ft 7in (12.67m); wing area 291 sq ft (27.03m²).
**Weights:** Empty 6,893lb (3,127kg); loaded 9,908lb (4,494kg), overload 14,444lb (6,552kg).
**Performance:** Maximum speed (clean) 281mph (452km/h) at sea level; initial climb (normal weight), 2,600ft (790m)/min; service ceiling 24,000ft (7.32km); take-off distance (normal weight) 740ft (226m); landing distance same; combat radius (max weapon load, low level, no loiter) 228 miles (367km); ferry range 1,382 miles (2,224km).
**Armament:** Carried on five external attachments, one on centreline rated at 1,200lb (544kg) and four rated at 600lb (272kg) on short body sponsons which also house four 7.62mm M60 machine guns with 500 rounds each.
**History:** First flight 16 July 1965, (production OV-10A) 6 August 1967; USAF combat duty June 1968.
**Users:** USA (Air Force, Marine Corps), West Germany, Indonesia, Morocco, Thailand, Venezuela.

This unique warplane was the chief tangible outcome of prolonged DoD studies in 1959-65 of Co-In (Counter-Insurgency) aircraft tailored to the unanticipated needs of so-called brushfire wars using limited weapons in rough terrain. The Marines issued a LARA (Light Armed Recon Aircraft) specification, which was won by NAA's NA-300 in August 1964. Features included a superb all-round view for the pilot and observer seated in tandem ejection seats, STOL rough-strip performance, and a rear cargo compartment usable by five paratroops or two casualties plus attendant. Of the initial batch of 271, the Air Force took 157 for use in the FAC role, deploying them immediately in Vietnam. Their ability to respond rapidly with light fire against surface targets proved very valuable, and the OV-10 was always popular and a delight to fly. In 1970, LTV Electrosystems modified 11 for night-FAC duty with sensors for detecting surface targets and directing accompanying attack aircraft, but most OV-10s now in use are of the original model. Units include TAC's 1st SOW at Hurlburt Field Florida; the 602nd TACW, Bergstrom AFB, Texas; the 601st TCW, Sembach AB, Germany; Pacaf's 51st CW, Osan, Korea; and certain specialized schools.

Six of the USAF aircraft were transferred to Morocco, and the other export customers were Indonesia (16 OV-10F), Thailand (40 OV-10C) and Venezuela (16 OV-10E). West Germany's Luftwaffe uses six OV-10Bs and 12 jet-boosted OV-10B(Z) target tugs. The US Marine Corps, one of the original customers, has withdrawn most OV-10s but retains 17 upgraded to OV-10D standard as NOS (Night Observation Surveillance) aircraft. Their long noses carry chin turrets with a laser target designator and FLIR which can be slaved to a ventral turret with a GE M197 three-barrel 20mm gun. Other equipment includes APR-39 RHAWS. ALE-39 chaff/flare cartridge dispensers and IR-suppressed engine jetpipes whilst the five external weapons points can lift a total of 3,600lb (1,632kg) when the aircraft operates in the attack role.

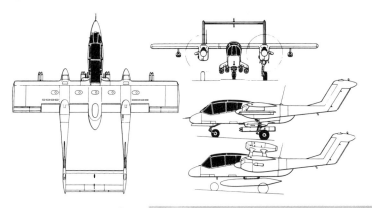

**Above:** Three-view of the OV-10A with lower side view showing the Luftwaffe OV-10B(Z).

**Right:** The OV-10A has proved a very popular tactical aircraft, with good manoeuvrability.

**Below:** Close-up of the nose of an OV-10D, showing the forward sensor turret and the rear weapon turret.

# Saab 37 Viggen

## SF37, SH37

**Origin:** Saab-Scania AB, Linköping, Sweden.
**Type:** Single-seat high-speed reconnaissance aircraft, (SF) armed overland, (SH) armed oversea.
**Powerplant:** One 26,015lb (11,800kg) thrust Svenska Flygmotor RM8A augmented turbofan.
**Dimensions:** Span 34ft 9¼in (10.6m); length 53ft 5¾in (16.3m); height 19ft 0¼in (5.8m); wing area (main wing) 490.1 sq ft (46m²).
**Weights:** Not disclosed, except gross weight normally between 33,070 and 44,090lb (15,000-20,000kg).
**Performance:** Maximum speed (clean) 912mph (1,468km/h, Mach 1.2) at sea level; over 1,320mph (2,124km/h, Mach 2) at high altitude; field length (no-flare landing) 1,640ft (500m).
**Armament:** Normally two RB24 Sidewinder AAMs on outer wing pylons for self-defence; air-to-ground or anti-ship weapons can be carried at the expense of sensors, tanks or EW pods.
**History:** First flight (AJ) 8 February 1967, (SF) 21 May 1973, (SH) 10 December 1973; service delivery (SF) April 1977, (SH) June 1975.
**Users:** Sweden.

System 37 is the most important item in the defence of Sweden, and it comprises a complete generation of combat aircraft produced in five versions sharing a near-common airframe. The original model was the AJ37 attack aircraft, which was followed by the SF37, SH37 and SK37 dual trainer, a total of 180 of these versions being delivered; they were followed by the JA37 interceptor, with much greater differences, which remains in production.

The SH37, for maritime use, replaced the S32C Lansen in F13 Wing and in mixed SH/SF Wings F17 and F21. It is used primarily to survey, register and report all maritime activity near Sweden. It has the basic airframe of the AJ37, with an LM Ericsson multimode radar, Marconi HUD and central digital computer, with an added camera for recording the radar displays. The three fuselage pylons carry a large tank on the centreline, a night reconnaissance pod with IR linescan and LLTV on the left and a Red

**Above: Both reconnaissance versions of the System 37 Viggen have a "chisel" type nose housing a forward oblique optical camera. This is an SF37 which has no nose radar (see text).**

Baron or long-range camera pod on the right. Inboard wing pylons can carry active or passive ECM jammer pods, and very complete Elint and EW recorders are carried, together with a tape recorder and a data camera which records film co-ordination figures, date, time, aircraft position, course, height, target location and other information.

The SF37, which serves with the same three wings as the SH, has no nose radar, and its slim, pointed nose houses four vertical or oblique cameras for low-level use, two long-range vertical high-altitude cameras and a VKA IR linescan. Also installed in the fuselage are the camera sight, an IR sensor and EW systems including an RWR and Elint recorders. The sensors give 180° horizon-to-horizon coverage and are specially arranged to work on wavelengths which reveal the presence of camouflaged targets. External loads can include the centreline tanks and active or passive ECM pods on the inboard wing pylons.

**Left: Another picture of an SF37 Viggen. A large drop tank is usually carried on the centreline, and reconnaissance pods can be hung on the fuselage side pylons. Here a Red Baron is seen on the right inboard pylon, with forward and oblique camera and IRLS (linescan) in the main section. These aircraft can carry a wide variety of photo, IR and ECM equipment. Note the ECM spiral-aerial receiver pods on the wing leading edges.**

55

# Tupolev Tu-20

## Tu-95 and 142, Bear-D and E

**Origin:** The OKB named for A.N. Tupolev, Soviet Union.
**Type:** (D) oceanic surveillance and ship targeting aircraft; (E) maritime reconnaissance aircraft.
**Powerplant:** Four 14,795shp Kuznetsov NK-12MV turboprops.
**Dimensions:** Span 167ft 8in (51.1m); length 155ft 10in (47.5m); height 39ft 9in (12.12m); wing area 3,342 sq ft (310.5m²).
**Weights:** Empty, about 167,550lb (76,000kg); maximum take-off 374,800lb (170,000kg).
**Performance:** Maximum speed (light weight) 525mph (845km/h) at high altitude; high speed cruise 435mph (700km/h); operating ceiling 44,300ft (13.5km); unrefuelled combat radius 5,150 miles (8,300km); endurance at 400mph (644km/h) 28 hours.
**Armament:** Defensive armament comprises three turrets each with two 23mm cannon; these versions do not normally carry offensive weapons.
**History:** First flight (Tu-95 prototype) 1954; service entry 1956, (D) possibly about 1963, (E) about 1965.
**Users:** Soviet Union (AV-MF).

A triumph in terms of aerodynamics (of the wing and the propellers), structure and certainly propulsion, this gigantic swept-wing machine is by far the fastest propeller-driven aircraft ever put into service, and it enabled the great power of the gas turbine to be combined with the economy of turboprop propulsion for global missions at a time when any jet engine inevitably meant short range. The original version, called Tu-20 by the DA (long-range aviation of the air force) and dubbed Bear-A by NATO, was a long-range free-fall bomber, with a normal internal bombload of 44,090lb

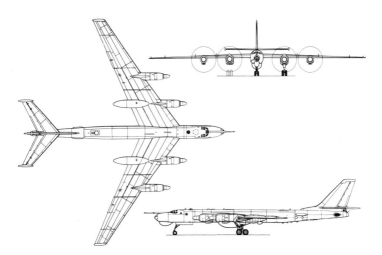

**Above: Three-view of Bear-D, one of the most widely encountered versions of this extremely successful long-range aircraft. Some have an EW-packed tail, with no turret.**

**Left: One of the best-ever photographs seen in the West of any Bear version, this Bear-D was being escorted by F-4E interceptors of the US Air Force in a long-range probing sortie over the Pacific. There has been much speculation on the exact equipment fit carried by these aircraft, but one basic factor is that there is abundant electric generating power and lifting capacity. The flight endurance of some 28 hours can be extended by use of the flight-refuelling probe, though crew efficiency would deteriorate after much longer periods in the air.**

(20,000kg). Six variants have been identified, those concerned with reconnaissance being designated Bear-D and Bear-E by NATO. The former, about 50 of which are still serving with the AV-MF (naval air force), retains most of the original bomber airframe but has a nose inflight-refuelling probe, chin radar for navigation and mapping, and a fuselage entirely devoted to maritime reconnaissance systems (plus a long-believed capability of providing mid-course guidance for long-range cruise missiles, notably SS-N-3 Shaddock, fired from friendly warships). ▶

► The dominant feature is a gigantic radar occupying the former bomb bay, with a giant 360° scanner but operating in I-band. There are nearly 40 other electronics aerials, including large blister fairings on each side of the rear fuselage, each over 9ft (2.74m) long, and a pod fairing on the tip of each horizontal tail. In 1978 one aircraft of this type was seen with the tail

**Right: Another Bear-D, one of the first of this series to be identified in the West in the mid-1960s, photographed by the US Navy over an oceanic area. One Western guess put the weight of electronic equipment carried at 14 tonnes (30,864lb).**

**Below: Latest, largest and heaviest of the known versions of Bear is the Tu-142, Bear-F, used for ASW missions by the AVMF (Soviet naval air force). This particular example, being escorted by USAF F-4E reconnaissance aircraft, has a large rear-facing fin antenna.**

turret (and associated extra-large I-band aft-facing radar) replaced by a long fairing housing additional electronics including Elint and ECM. Bear-E is a photo-reconnaissance model with six (occasionally seven) belly windows for large vertical and oblique optical cameras, with the same glazed nose and rear-fuselage blisters.

# Tupolev Tu-22

## Tu-22 Blinder-A, C

**Origin:** The OKB named for A.N. Tupolev, Soviet Union.
**Type:** (A) bomber-reconnaissance; (C) maritime reconnaissance aircraft.
**Powerplant:** Two large afterburning turbojets, believed to be 30,865lb
(14,000kg) thrust Koliesov VD-7F.
**Dimensions (estimated):** Span 90ft 10½in (27.7m); length 132ft 11½in
(40.53m); height 35ft (10.67m); wing area 1,650 sq ft (153m²).
**Weights (estimated):** Empty 90,700lb (40,000kg); internal fuel 79,360lb
(36,000kg); maximum take-off 185,000lb (84,000kg).
**Performance (estimated):** Maximum speed (clean) 920mph (1,480km/h),
Mach 1.4) at high altitude, 550mph (890km/h) at sea level; combat radius
(all-hi) 1,926 miles (3,100km); ferry range 4,040 miles (6,500km).
**Armament:** One 23mm radar-directed gun for tail defence; (A) internal
bay for free-fall bombload of about 17,600lb (8,000kg) (considereably
more with reduced fuel), (C) no offensive stores.
**History:** First flight (Tu-105 prototype) 1959, (production Tu-22) probably
1963.
**Users:** Soviet Union, Iraq, Libya.

Above: Tu-22 Blinder-C showing camera apertures along underside.

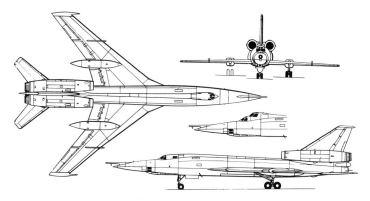

**Above: Three-view of Blinder-A with (inset) nose of Blinder-D trainer.**

**Below: Blinder-A free-fall bomber, most of which operate unpainted. The multi-sensor Blinder-C is similar.**

For 20 years the estimated range of this large and heavy supersonic aircraft published in Western sources was ludicrously low (typically a "maximum range of 1,400 miles"); in fact, though it was never designed to fly intercontinental round-trip missions, the Tu-22 has sufficient range and endurance to cover the entire oceanic area from Soviet bases to beyond the North Pole and as far as Greenland, and its ceiling of some 60,000ft (18km) makes it very difficult to intercept.

Blinder-A was built in small numbers but is believed still to be in service, mainly as a multisensor reconnaissance aircraft, the bulk of the AV-MF (naval air force) strength of attack versions comprising 125 of the missile-armed B version. Blinder-C is the dedicated oceanic surveillance version, of which about 60 were delivered and 40 remain operational. The weapons bay houses various reconnaissance systems, including six large optical cameras with windows in the double-fold doors. At least one aircraft has a giant SLAR, and it would be reasonable to suppose that IR linescan and SAR installations are flying, though evidence is lacking in the West. Since 1980 the number of externally identified aerials (antennae) on Blinder-C has grown from about 20 to more than 25, and NATO opinion is coming round to the view that these impressive aircraft are now being used chiefly in Elint roles. Reconnaissance and EW systems appear to be controlled by the occupant of the lower forward cockpit with downward-ejection seat immediately aft of the nose mapping and navigation radar.

All models have inflight-refuelling capability. The AV-MF operates many of its Tu-22s from bases in Estonia to cover the Baltic, with others in the southern Ukraine for missions over the Mediterranean.

**Left: A recent, and unusual, photograph of a Blinder-A free-fall bomber, with inflight-refuelling probe removed. If the USAF B-58 is a true guide, cost of Tu-22 operations must be extremely high.**

# EW Aircraft

Something in excess of one million reconnaissance flights were made in World War I. The tools used were a note-pad and camera, and sometimes a special bag or canister in which to drop from the sky either the observer's message or the exposed film, which was usually in the form of metal-boxed glass plates. Only at the very end of that war were aerial radio sets brought into use. The idea of using radio signals as weapons followed naturally from the invention of radar before World War II. By 1944 the RAF, far more than any other armed force in the world, had carried EW (electronic warfare) into practice on an impressive scale.

Today, after 30 years of playing second fiddle to bullets and bombs, EW systems are all the rage among air forces who, in the main, have no idea of what was going on in 1944. Not only are the techniques of jamming hostile radars with chaff—the basic and most widely used form of electronic counter-measures (ECM) — having to be re-learnt, but also the methods required to distort the enemy's electronic measurements, to confuse his radar operators, and to use electrical power to create EM signals of just the right type, sent out only at the required moments of time, and emitted in only the right directions to be effective. Powerful jammers can blanket the enemy's wavelengths, either by broad-band jamming, which is essentially a "brute force and ignorance" method and which can affect friend as much as foe, or by the more selective spot jamming techniques which can prevent the enemy from "locking on": radar warning receivers (RWR) are carried to indicate when the aircraft is being illuminated by a hostile radar, and advanced equipments give details about the nature

of the illumination, identify the type of radar and indicate its exact location, ECM then being brought in to negate the threat.

Before we can indulge in EW we have to know as much as we can about the enemy's emissions. This calls for thorough Elint (electronic intelligence) surveillance 24 hours a day, covering all the enemy's emitters both geographically and in spread of wavelengths. We can then build up a library of his emitters so that, each time a signal is detected, even if only for a split second, our EW systems can identify its source. We are concerned not only with all kinds of radars, on the land, on board ships and in the air, but also with communications, electronic navigation aids and many other forms of emitters. We are also interested not only in radio wavelengths but also in the much shorter wavelengths known as IR (infra-red) and in those shorter still which we call light and which enable us to see.

Modern airspace is becoming so electronically perilous that even the latest tactical aircraft have little hope of survival without a counter-vailing electronic defensive system. This is especially so in Eastern Europe, where the heaviest air defence systems in the world are deployed. For example, there are several areas in Warsaw Pact airspace where a NATO aircraft flying at an altitude of 10,000ft (3,000m) could be caught in the beams of one thousand surface-based radars simultaneously, with rapid-fire guns, surface-to-air missiles (SAMs) and interceptor aircraft all waiting to be triggered by the radar responses.

It is not appropriate here to discuss optical countermeasures, which include camouflage paint, low-visibility single-colour schemes, attempts to confuse by painting

**Above: Preparing to launch an EA-6B Prowler from USS *America*. Like the A-7E Corsairs (of VA-87, the Golden Warriors), it belongs to carrier wing CVW-6, in the US Navy's Atlantic Fleet.**

false cockpit canopies on the undersides of fighters and even the use of smokescreens. IRCM (infra-red countermeasures) has not yet given rise to a special category of dedicated aircraft, but it has led to battlefield helicopters and close-support aircraft shielding or cooling their engine nozzles, and to all kinds of combat aircraft having the capability of carrying false IR sources, either on pylons or in packaged payloads which can be ejected from an on-board dispenser. These bright flares, it is hoped, form a more attractive target to an IR-homing missile than the aircraft itself.

All tactical aircraft today must have some EW capability. But the aircraft described in the following pages are those whose primary purpose is EW, often to the exclusion of other forms of weapon. Such machines are extremely expensive, and they remain a relatively rare breed for the time being. As the threat increases, however, and as the cost of electronic equipment becomes effectively lower, these aircraft may become more affordable in the future. Meanwhile, apart from a few training aircraft, all the EW platforms are concentrated in the air forces of the USA and the USSR.

At first glance this may not appear serious. Aircraft that fire bullets and missiles probably seem more important than those that fire nothing but electromagnetic radiation. Yet such an assessment is certainly superficial. In the modern world the EW platform is at least as important as any other kind of weapon in the inventory.

As an example, the fact that the RAF has no EW aircraft other than a few aged Canberras used in the ECM training role should be a matter for great British public concern. Such ageing aircraft as the Canberra, Shackleton and Britannia could all have been packed with very high-power jammers, or comprehensive Elint receivers and recorders, in the same way that their counterparts have been in the Soviet Union. That this has not been done is due largely to shortage of money.

# Aeritalia G222

## G222VS

**Origin:** Aeritalia SAI, Italy.
**Type:** Electronic-warfare version of military transport.
**Powerplant:** Two 3,400shp Fiat-built General Electric T64-P4D turboprops (also available with 4,860shp Rolls-Royce Tyne Mk 801 turboprops).
**Dimensions:** Span 94ft 2in (28.7m); length 74ft 5½in (22.7m); height 32ft 1¾in (9.8m); wing area 882.6sq ft (82m²).
**Weights:** Empty about 34,000lb (15,422kg); maximum loaded 61,730lb (28,000kg).
**Performance:** Maximum speed not stated but less than normal transport's 336mph (540km/h); operating height, up to 29,000ft (8.84km); normal mission endurance 10hr.
**Armament:** None.
**History:** First flight (G222) 18 July 1970, (G222VS) 9 March 1978.
**Users:** Reported adopted by Italy.

Widely sold as a light military cargo airlifter, the G222 is small enough to be economically interesting for such roles as EW jamming, Elint, navaid calibration and martime surveillance. The G222VS is the basic EW variant, with uprated (twin 40kVA generators) electrical system and a main cabin provided with extensive racking for receiving, processing, analysing, identifying, locating and storing hostile signals. A rotodome aerial is fitted above the fin, and there is also a small radar in a thimble radome beneath the nose. The VS is said to be useful in the AWAC mission, as well as RPV launch

**Above:** The main distinguishing feature of the Aeritalia G222VS is its small "doughnut" rotodome aerial with surveillance, IFF and data-link elements, which rotates above the fin. No production has been officially announced.

and remote piloting, and one load in this role is up to six Meteor Mirach 100 vehicles (as described in the RPVs section), together with a remote pilot station. A French report suggests that two of the Italian G222 aircraft are of this VS version, used mainly for Elint and ESM missions, though this has not been officially confirmed. The G222RM is a version for calibrating navaids and ILS systems.

**Below:** The G222VS has a flight crew of two in the nose cockpit and up to ten systems operators at consoles in the cabin.

# Antonov An-12

## An-12 Cub-B, C

**Origin:** The OKB named for Oleg K. Antonov.
**Type:** (Cub-B) Elint aircraft; (Cub-C) ECM aircraft; (Cub-?) airborne command post.
**Engines:** Four 4,190ehp Ivchyenko AI-20M single-shaft turboprops.
**Dimensions:** Span 124ft 8in (38m); length (normal) 108ft 7¼in (33.1m); height 34ft 6½in (10.53m); wing area 1,310 sq ft (121.7m²).
**Weights:** Empty (basic) 61,730lb (28,000kg); maximum payload 44,090lb (20,000kg); loaded 121,475lb (55,100kg); maximum loaded 134,480lb (61,000kg).
**Performance:** Maximum speed (normal weight, medium altitude), 482mph (777km/h); maximum cruising speed 416mph (670km/h); economical cruise 365mph (587km/h); minimum flying speed 101mph (163km/h); take-off distance (normal weight, paved runway) 2,295ft (700m); initial climb 1,970ft (600m)/min; service ceiling 33,460ft (10.2km); range (max payload), 2,236 miles (3,600km), (maximum fuel) 3,542 miles (5,700km).
**Armament:** (Cub-B) tail turret with two NR-23 guns, (Cub-C) none.
**History:** First flight believed 1958; service delivery 1959; termination of production 1973.
**Users:** Soviet Union.

It is estimated that some 850 examples of the basic An-12BP transport aircraft were built, of which about 720 were supplied to the VTA. Although now supplemented by the Il-76, at least 500 An-12s remain in

service, and a small number of these have been converted into Elint platforms for the Soviet Naval Air Force to detect, monitor, record and analyse electronic signals from NATO ships, aircraft and ground forces. Designated "Cub-B" by NATO, they retain the tail turret but have a cabin filled with electronics and operator consoles. At least 14 additional antennae have been identified, mostly on the fuselage.

The ECM model, called Cub-C, is a more extensive rebuild, with the rear turret replaced by a large dielectric radome. Several high-power jammers are fitted, with their antennae in canoe-type blisters on the underside of the fuselage and ahead of the main undercarriage fairings. The aircraft also has bulged rear doors. About 30 of this version were produced and they serve with the VVS and AVMF. At least one of this type has been seen wearing Egyptian insignia.

The basic aircraft is exactly comparable to the C-130 Hercules, and was derived from the civil An-10 Ukraina of 1957 by redesigning the rear fuselage to incorporate a full-width rear ramp and loading doors and a rear turret. The large, circular-section fuselage is pressurised and air-conditioned, and the landing-gear is designed for use on unpaved surfaces.

Recent Western Press reports suggest that Soviet forces are making increased use of airborne command posts for the ground forces (at army, front and theatre level), for the naval forces and at national level. In an exercise in 1983 these airborne command posts, the majority of which are An-12s, practised communications both with their subordinates and with each other.

**Below: An-12s engaged in intelligence activities have been seen with both military (AVMF) and civil Aeroflot markings. This Cub-B has no markings beyond civil registration, but retains tail armament. Some 14 Elint aerials (antennae) can be seen along the fuselage.**

# Beech Super King Air

## RC-12D, RU-21H, RU-21J

**Origin:** Beech Aircraft Corporation, Wichita, Kansas.
**Type:** "Special mission" aircraft. (Following specifications refer to RC-12D).
**Powerplant:** Two 801ehp Pratt & Whitney PT6A-38 turboprops.
**Dimensions:** Span 54ft 6in (16.61m), (RC-12D) 57ft 10in (17.63m); length 43ft 9in (13.34m); wing area 303 sq ft (28.15m$^2$).
**Weights:** Empty 7,800lb (3,538kg); loaded 12,500lb (5,670kg), (RU-21J) 15,000lb (6,804kg).
**Performance:** Maximum cruising speed 272mph (437km/h) at 30,000ft (9.45km); range (max cruising speed) 1,824 miles (2,935km); take-off/landing distance about 2,800ft (850m).
**Armament:** None.
**History:** First flight (company prototype) 27 October 1972; first military contract August 1974.
**Users:** USA (Army).

The US Army has procured at least three versions of the Beech King Air/Super King Air series of utility twin-engined aircraft for use in "special mission" work. The first was the RC-21A (King Air 100), of which at least two aircraft are still operational. These are fitted with the ARQ-38 Left Jab radio direction finding (RDF) system which operates in the range 20-150MHz.

The latest variant is the RU-21J, of which three were delivered in 1974 under the Cefly Lancer programme. These aircraft have a large number of external antennae and obviously carry much extra equipment as they are cleared for take-off at 15,000lb (6,804kg), which is 2,500lb (1,134kg) above other versions. Among the equipment known to be carried by the RU-21J are the ALQ-150, ALQ-151 and ALQ-156, together with the ARQ-28 described above. The ALQ-150 is a tactical ESM equipment for use against multichannel microwave systems, which are used by the Warsaw Pact armies for higher level trunk communications. Interestingly, the three RU-21Js seem to cover different frequency bands: aircraft one covers 60-115MHz and 1,500-9,000MHz, aircraft two 115-480MHz and aircraft three 450-1,500MHz. This means that constant jamming over a

**Above: Beech RU-21D, with Elint systems similar to RU-21E, of 1971.**

protracted period is not possible. ALQ-151 (Quick Fix) is a DF intercept and ECM system operating in the 2-76MHz range which is also fitted to the EH-1G and EH-60A. The RU-21J is also fitted with the ALQ-156 Missile Detector System which evaluates threats and automatically deploys decoys from an M-130 flare dispenser Such a system implies that the RU-21J will be flying sufficiently close to the front-line to become a target for Warsaw Pact SAMs.

Guardrail V, a combined airborne and ground communications system, is designed to intercept and locate hostile communication emitters. The current aircraft is the RU-21H, but this is being replaced by the larger, faster and more capable RC-12D, the military version of the Super King Air. The RC-12D's main equipment is the ALQ-162 Compass Sail continuous-wave (CW) jammer and is intended to defeat Warsaw Pact CW-type missiles such as SA-6. The ALQ-136, an I/J-band radar jammer is also fitted, as a counter to equipments such as the Gun Dish radar on ZSU-23-4 and SA-9. ALQ-156 is also carried. It would appear that the RC-12D is optimised for the anti-missile role and would be deployed in support of airborne operations in enemy forward areas.

**Left: One of the three Beech RU-21J (based on the Super King Air 200) aircraft delivered to the US Army in 1974 under the Cefly Lancer programme. They are packed with speical intelligence electronic systems and are cleared to operate at weights up to 15,000lb (6,804kg), compared with 12,500lb (5,670kg) for other Super King Air models. PT6A turbo-prop engines are rated at 850shp.**

# Boeing C-135 family

**Origin:** Boeing Airplane Company (from May 1961 The Boeing Company), Seattle, Washington.
**Type:** EW, Elint, command-post and strategic reconnaisance aircraft.
**Powerplant:** (A and derivatives) four 13,750lb (6,273kg) thrust Pratt & Whitney J57-59W or 43WB turbojets; (B and derivatives) four 18,000lb (8,165kg) thrust Pratt & Whitney TF33-3 turbofans; (RE) four 22,000lb (9,979kg) thrust CFM56-1B11 turbofans.
**Dimensions:** Span (basic) 130ft 10in (39.88m); length (basic) 134ft 6in (40.99m); height (basic) 38ft 4in (11.68m), (tall fin) 41ft 8in (12.69m); wing area 2,433sq ft (226m²).
**Weights:** Empty (KC-135A basic) 98,466lb (44,664kg), (KC, operating weight) 106,306lb (48,220kg), (C-135B) 102,300lb (46,403kg); loaded (KC, original) 297,000lb (134,719kg), (KC, later max) 316,000lb (143,338kg), (C-135B) 275,000lb (124,740kg) (typical of special variants).
**Performance:** Maximum speed (all) about 580mph (933km/h); typical high-speed cruise, 532mph (856km/h) at 35,000ft (10.7km); initial climb (J57, typical) 1,290ft (393m)/min, (TF33) 4,900ft (1,494m)/min; service ceiling (KC, full load) 36,000ft (10.9km), (C-135B) 44,000ft (13.4km); mission radius (KC) 3,450 miles (5,552km) to offload 24,000lb (10,886kg) transfer fuel, 1,150 miles (1,950km) to offload 120,000lb (54,432kg); field length (KC,ISA+17°C) 13,700ft (4,176m).
**Armament:** None.
**History:** First flight 31 August 1956, (variants) see text.
**Users:** USA (mainly Air Force).

Boeing risked more than the company's net value to build a prototype jet airliner, first flown in July 1954. An important factor behind the gamble was the belief that the USAF would buy a jet tanker/transport to replace

**Above: The Boeing EC-135J is just one of many variants of the C-135 family. It is used as a strategic command and communications platform, this particular example serving with PacAf (USAF Pacific Air Forces).**

the Boeing KC-97 family, and this was justified by the announcement of an initial order for 29 aircraft only three weeks after the company prototype flew and long before it had done any inflight refuelling tests. The KC-135A Stratotanker differed only in minor respects from the original prototype, and deliveries began on 30 April 1957, building up to 20 per month and eventually reaching a grand total of 732 aircraft.    ▶

**Below: Very closely related to the EC-135J above, the EC-135C is another airborne command post with special communications installations. Used by USAF Strategic Air Command, they have a saddle radome above the fuselage, HF probe aerials (antennae) on the wingtips, various VHF and UHF blade aerials and a long trailing wire from under the fuselage. The refuelling boom is retained, but the engines are TF33 turbofans.**

▶ The basic KC-135A has a windowless main fuselage with 80 tip-up passenger seats and a cargo floor with tie-down fittings. Fuel is carried in 12 wing tanks and a further nine in the fuselage, of which only one, that in the extreme tail, is above the main floor level. The KC-135 force numbers 615 active aircraft in 35 squadrons, including 80 aircraft in Reserve units. Other versions followed on the production line, ending with ten RC-135Bs; when the line closed in February 1965, 808 C-135s of all types had been built for the USAF.

Since then the family has swollen by modification to become one of the most diverse in aviation history. Of special interest are the specialised reconnaissance (RC-135 series) and electronic/command post (EC-135 series) versions. These include the EC-135A radio link (SAC post-attack command and control system); EC-135B, Air Force Systems Command (ex-RIA, range instrumentation aircraft, now twice converted); EC-135C, SAC command post; EC-135G, ICBM launch and radio link (with boom); EC-135H, airborne command post; EC-135J, airborne command post for Pacific Air Force; EC-135K, airborne command post for Tactical Air Command; EC-135L, special SAC relay platform; EC-135N (now C-135N), for Apollo range duties; EC-135P, communications/command post; KC-135A, original designation retained for SAC relay links; KC-135R (also known as RC-135R), for special reconnaissance/EW tasks; RC-135B and RC-135C, reconnaissance aircraft with SLAR cheeks and other sensors; RC-135D, with different SLARs and thimble nose; RC-135E, with glassfibre forward fuselage and inboard wing pods; RC-135M, with special electronic installations and turbofan engines; RC-135S, similar to M; RC-135T, one-off special aircraft for SAC; RC-135U, with special sensors and antennae covering the entire airframe, including SLAR cheeks, extended tailcone and various chin, dorsal, ventral and fin antennae; RC-135V, seven Cs and one U rebuilt with nose thimble, wire antennae and ventral blades; and, finally, RC-135W, mostly rebuilt Ms with SLAR cheeks added. ▶

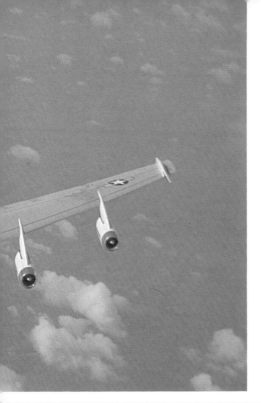

Left: Taken from a closely related KC-135A tanker, this EC-135H is unusual in having J57 turbojet engines and not the TF33 turbofans more commonly fitted to these relay versions.

Below: Distinguished by its large drooped nose radar, the EC-135N series came in several versions, this example having J57 engines and a small dorsal blister, plus wingtip probes.

Foot of page: Possibly taken at Patrick AFB, Cape Canaveral, this shows several electronic versions of the KC/C-135 family. Nearest the camera is an N.

► A typical application of this remarkably adaptable airframe is the EC-135A post-attack command and control system (PACCS) for SAC, known as the Looking Glass mission. This task has been flown continuously since 3 February 1961, involving three aircraft per day, each on a flight lasting 8 hours or more. The task commander, designated Airborne Emergency Actions Officer (AEAO), is a general officer (i.e. a brigadier-general or above) from SAC, and he is assisted by a battle staff, communications specialists, technicians and the flight crew.

The command, control and communications ($C^3$) fit is very sophisticated and is being continuously updated, but it is constrained by the size of the aircraft. There is a UHF link to the Air Force Satellite Communications System (AFSATCOM), using an omni-directional antenna beneath a streamlined radome on the fuselage roof. The aircraft has numerous ►

**Left: Large cheek SLARs adorn the RC-135U, together with rows of dipole aerials, tip probes and tail installations.**

**Below: A closely related variant, the RC-135V is another SLAR fan-engined platform, again with modified wingtips and tail.**

▶ communications links, including those to SAC's underground command posts, the headquarters of the 8th and 15th Air Forces, various airfields, other SAC aircraft on ground and airborne alert (e.g. B-52 bombers and other C³ aircraft), Titan and Minuteman launch control centres and the Emergency Rocket Communications System.

As in all other nuclear weapons command systems, the Looking Glass mission has stringent controls. In this case the Airborne Launch Control

**Above: Photographed in the early 1970s in the heyday of the special variants of the C-135, this RC-135V was powered by TF33 engines and served as a special multisensor reconnaissance platform with USAF Strategic Air Command. Features included a large forward-looking nose radar, giant cheek SLAR installations, numerous dorsal bumps, wingtip HF communications probes and a tail cut off short, the refuelling boom being removed.**

System (ALCS) must first be activated by the aircraft commander, who must be satisfied that a valid emergency message has been received; he then switches on the system. ALCS still requires two key turns for launch orders to be issued: one key is held by the AEAO and the other by the communications officer, these two sitting at opposite ends of the battle staff compartmet. Accidental or mischievous activation is thus presented, as in land-based control centres.

Below: Another SAC special reconnaissance model was the RC-135U, which again had fan engines but retained the original nose radar. Note chin and ventral radar and the blister ahead of the former FR boom.

# English Electric (BAe) Canberra

## Canberra T Mk 17

**Origin:** English Electric Company (now BAe), UK.
**Type:** ECM/ECCM aircraft.
**Powerplant:** Two 7,500lb (3,400kg) Rolls-Royce Avon 109 turbojets.
**Dimensions:** Span 63ft 11in (19.5m); length 65ft 6in (19.95m); height 15ft 7in (4.72m); wing area 960sq ft (89.19m²).
**Weights:** Maximum take-off 42,500lb (19,278kg).
**Performance:** Maximum speed Mach 0.83; service ceiling 48,000ft (14.6km); range (tactical radius at low level) 805 miles (1,300km).
**Armament:** None.
**History:** First flight (Canberra B Mk 1) 13 May 1949.
**Users:** UK (RAF).

**Right: Like hundreds of other Canberras, the T.17s have been back to British Aerospace Aircraft Group's factory at Samlesbury, near Preston, for updating and refurbishing. Here a T.17 is seen almost ready for redelivery to 360 Sqn.**

**Below: One of 24 Canberra B.2s converted into T.17 ECM aircraft, with nose installations of active jammers broadly similar to those in the tail of the Vulcan, with spiral-antenna emitters under each blister.**

One of the few remaining versions of the venerable English Electric Canberra still in service with the RAF is the Mk 17, serving with 360 Squadron at RAF Wyton. This aircraft has a very sophisticated ECM/ESM fit and is manned by mixed crews from both the RAF and the RN. Although used mainly for the peacetime training of British forces in ECCM tasks, these aircraft clearly have a potential ECM/ESM task in wartime. They are to be supplemented in due course by a small number of BAe 125 aircraft specially fitted out for the ECM/ESM training role.

The RAF does not possess a combat aircraft dedicated to this role on the lines of the EA-6B or EF-111A, partly on grounds of economics — the fly-away price of an EA-6B is approximately £38 million ($57.8 million) at 1983 prices. A second reason, however, is that the RAF does not envisage massive raids requiring dedicated ECM aircraft to open up electronic corridors, such as were carried out by the USAF in Vietnam. Instead, primary reliance will be placed upon ECM pods to enable individual aircraft to make their own way through the enemy's electronic defences.

To meet the urgent need of the British ground forces in Germany (1 Corps) for real-time information on what is happening in Warsaw Pact territory, at present provided by sporadic missions by a handful of manned

aircraft which must not cross the frontier, it is planned to deploy two types of sensor carried in three types of vehicle. Most numerous will be the Phoenix RPV (described in the RPV section), but the manned aircraft will comprise about 12 special Westland Lynx helicopters and seven Canberra PR Mk 9 aircraft, all of which will be fitted with advanced radars in a programme called Castor (Corps Airborne Stand-Off Radar). The fixed-wing jet will fly at an extreme altitude of some 60,000ft (18.3km) carrying a high-definition SAR (Synthetic-Aperture Radar) probably supplied by Thorn-EMI and using some elements from Searchwater with MTI and a beam width of 3.1 or 6.2 miles (5 or 10km) out to a range of 31 miles (50km), the great height giving a less acutely inclined picture at extreme range and thus smaller shadows. The helicopters will probably carry a sector-scanning derivative of the Blue Kestrel radar. Both radars would use MTI (Moving-Target Indication) and feed pictures direct to ground stations supplying the BATES and Wavell data-processing nets.

# General Dynamics/Grumman EF-111

## EF-111A

**Origin:** General Dynamics Corporation, Fort Worth, Texas; Grumman Aerospace Corporation, Bethpage, NY.

**Type:** EW aircraft.

**Powerplant:** Two 18,500lb (8,390kg) thrust Pratt & Whitney TF30-3 afterburning turbofans.

**Dimensions:** Span (fully spread) 63ft (19.2m), (fully swept) 31ft 11½in (9.74m); length 77ft 1½in (23.51m); wing area (gross, 16°) 525 sq ft (48.77m²).

**Weights:** Empty 53,418lb (24,230kg); loaded 87,478lb (39,680kg).

**Performance:** Maximum speed 1,160mph (1,865km/h, Mach 1.75) at 36,000ft (11km); cruising speed (penetration) 571mph (919km/h); initial climb 3,592ft (1,095m)/min; service ceiling (combat weight, max afterburner) 54,700ft (16.67km); range (max internal fuel) 2,484 miles (3,998km); take-off distance 3,250ft (991m).

**Armament:** None.

**History:** First flight (F-111A) 21 December 1964; service delivery (A) June 1967, (EF) 10 March 1977.

**Users:** USA (Air Force).

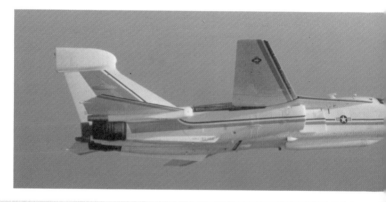

**Above: Grumman retained the first EF-111A "Electric Fox" at Calverton for numerous essential test programmes.**

Having become aware of the urgent need for a dedicated EW aircraft in the late 1960s, the USAF first studied a modified EB-66 for what was known as the Interim Tac Early Warning System (ITEWS). This proved to be a costly and, in the end, impracticable solution. The next study, in 1968-70, concentrated on a buy of Navy EA-6B Prowlers (*qv*) which package the powerful and very effective ALQ-99 EW system into A-6 airframes stretched to accommodate two extra aircrew. The USAF faulted the EA-6B because it does not have a supersonic capability, although it is arguable how often such a performance would be needed on operations. Second, criticism focused on a lack of range, and again this is arguable. Third, the EA-6B was said to be too expensive, but this is relative, and it is, in any ▶

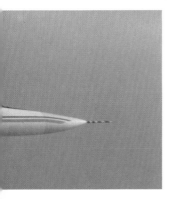

**Left: At one time 66-049, one of the EF-111A development aircraft, was painted in this non-standard colour scheme. This view shows the ALQ-99E canoe radar under the belly, serving the large ECM jammer group installed in the former weapons bay. The photo was taken at Grumman's Calverton, NY, facility in June 1978.**

**Below: The first EF-111 delivered to TAC was the twice-rebuilt 66-041, seen here with MO tail code after arrival at Mountain Home AFB, Idaho, in January 1982.**

▶ case, difficult to compare a new-build airframe with a conversion. Perhaps the real reason was that the Air Force just did not want to accept yet another naval aircraft design.

It was partly a matter of chance that it was found possible to convert the F-111 into an EW platform, even though it was said at the time that this would be not only the most cost-effective but also the lowest-risk solution. Grumman, the Navy's prime contractor for the EA-6B, was at first by no means certain that the conversion was possible, a particular problem being the need for two extra seats with neither unacceptable aerodynamic penalties nor severe effects on the aircraft's range. .Considerable improvements in the electronic suite, however, not only made the ALQ-99 able to handle hostile threats more quickly but also, by means of increased automation, enabled the operating crew to be reduced to one man. This system, the ALQ-99E, features inflight-adaptable antennae, digital jamming, and the complete isolation of active and passive systems: the ALQ-99E jamming subsystem detects, identifies, locates, records and, where desired, jams every kind of hostile emitter using computer control over direction and time. It is generally considered to be the best EW system in the world at present. ▶

**Right: In regular USAF service the EF-111A is painted plain grey, though unit badges are permitted. This was the first to become operational at Mountain Home AFB, at first with the 366th TFW and finally with the 388th EWS (Electronic Warfare Squadron). The biggest test of the Electric Fox is in Europe, where the Warsaw Pact air defences surpass anything that can be simulated in the Western world.**

**Below: The left-hand side of the EF-111A cockpit, occupied by the pilot, is not very different from that of the attack versions. The right-hand side, nearest the camera, is totally redesigned. The TFR (terrain-following radar) and attack radar scopes are supplemented by a giant rectangular radar display which can be used to print out locations and characteristics of most hostile emitters.**

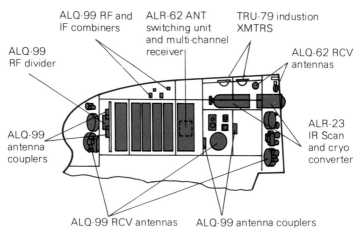

ALQ-99 RF and IF combiners
ALR-62 ANT switching unit and multi-channel receiver
TRU-79 industion XMTRS
ALQ-99 RF divider
ALQ-62 RCV antennas
ALQ-99 antenna couplers
ALR-23 IR Scan and cryo converter
ALQ-99 RCV antennas
ALQ-99 antenna couplers

**Above: To a considerable degree the fin cap installation of the EF-111A is the same as that of the EA-6B Prowler, though like the rest of the aircraft it is a little later in development timing. The RCV (receive) antennas serving the main ALQ-99 system face to all points of the compass. ALR-23 warns of IR (heat) sources.**

▶ Turning an F-111A into an EF-111A (unofficially nicknamed "Electric Fox") is a major rebuild operation. The main charges are the fin receivers and the installation of the jamming equipment pallet. Canadair supplies the fin, which is reinforced to carry 370lb (168kg) of pod structure loaded with 583lb (264kg) of electronic equipment. Grumman assembles the main jammer installation which, mounted on its pallet, weighs 4,274lb (1,939kg), while the canoe radome and door add a further 464lb (210kg). The EF-111A, therefore, flies like an F-111A with a 6,000lb (2,700kg) bomb load, and on "Red Flag" and other exercises the aircraft has repeatedly demonstrated its ability to fly in formation with F-111As on high-speed attack runs.

Forty-two EF-111As have been ordered; of these, 24 are assigned to the 388th Electronic Combat Squadron at Mountain Home in the USA and 12 to a second ECS at RAF Upper Heyford in England. A further six aircraft will be held against training and attrition requirements. In the future it is likely that the EF-111A will be fitted with JTIDS, which will enable it to establish real-time, secure links with ground stations or with AWACS aircraft. It is worth noting that the UK-based EF-111As represent the only combat EW force in Western Europe.

**Below: A close-up of the fin cap of one of the first EF-111A aircraft to join the US Air Force. The aft-facing window serves the sensitive heat receiver in the ALR-23 system which gives warning of IR sources, as well as their approximate bearing and elevation, so that appropriate self-defence action may be taken.**

# Grumman EA-6 Prowler

## EA-6B

**Origin:** Grumman Aerospace Corporation, Bethpage, NY.
**Type:** EW aircraft.
**Powerplant:** Two 11,200lb (5,080kg) thrust Pratt & Whitney J52-P-408 turbojets.
**Dimensions:** Span 53ft (16.15m); length 59ft 10in (18.24m); height 16ft 3in (4.95m); wing area 528.9 sq ft (49.1m²).
**Weights:** Empty 32,162lb (14,588kg); maximum take-off weight 65,000lb (29,483kg).
**Performance:** Maximum speed (clean) 651mph (1,048km/h) at sea level, (with 5 ECM pods) 623mph (1,002km/h); service ceiling (clean) 44,500ft (13.6km), (with 5 ECM pods) 38,000ft (11.6km); combat range 2,399 miles (3,861km).
**Armament:** None.
**History:** First flight (YA2F-1) 19 April 1960, (EA-6B) 25 May 1968.
**Users:** USA (Navy, Marine Corps).

The airframe of the Grumman A-6 has been used as the basis for an extremely successful tactical electronic warfare aircraft, the four-seat EA-6B Prowler. This aircraft has a 4ft 6in (1.37m) nose extension to accommodate two extra crewmen, and a large pod on top of the fin. The basic equipment of the EA-6B is the AN/ALQ-99 Tactical Jamming System (TJS), which is housed in five integrally powered pods (two under each wing, one under the fuselage) containing jamming transmitters; surveillance receivers are in the fin-tip pod. The ALQ-99 has three operating modes:

**Right: Like their single-seat Intruder attack counterparts, the US Navy and Marine Corps EA-6B Prowlers are gaily painted with unit liveries. This EA-6B bears Modex number 620 and serves with squadron VAQ-134.**

**Above: Coming in at low level over land, this EA-6B is equipped with three jamming pods and two long-range drop tanks.**

automatic, in which the computer selects the threat and takes the necessary action; semi-automatic, in which the computer ranks the threats in order of importance and the operators select the response; and manual, in which the operators carry out both search and jamming tasks. Typical power output for the jammers is 2kW, using spot, dual-spot, swept-spot and noise jamming.

From the 22nd EA-6B onwards, an Increased Capability (ICAP) fit is standard, and Grumman has since retrofitted the first twenty-one. ICAP ▶

**Left: This photograph shows that Modex 611 was serving aboard USS *Forrestal* with electronic-warfare squadron VAQ-130 as part of carrier air wing CVW-11; aircraft BuAer No is 160791. Compared with the single-seat A-6E the EA-6B can operate at higher weights, but has a more powerful version of the same J52 engine. Note the four crew-members, whereas only a pilot and EW officer are needed to run almost the same jamming system in the USAF EF-111A.**

▶ includes an expanded on-board tactical jamming system, better response times and improved displays and communications systems. An ICAP-2 version is now being fitted to all aircraft, and an Advanced Capability (ACAP) programme is under way.

Total procurement of this excellent aircraft is likely to be 102 (including four pre-production and one research and development airframe). Delivery started in January 1971 and production is expected to continue at a rate of six aircraft per year until 1986. It is illustrative of the expense of modern EW systems that an EA-6B costs £38.6 million ($57.8 million) at 1983 prices, a bill which very few other nations could afford.

Developed much later than the basically similar Blackburn (BAe) Buccaneer, the A-6 does not have the advanced airframe of the British aircraft and thus has a long-span wing which is not totally suitable for full-throttle operations at low level. Nevertheless the airframe—like all Grumman machines built like a battleship—is immensely strong and absorbs with ease the stresses of low flying and of carrier operations.

**Below: An EA-6B Prowler of a US Navy squadron about to be catapulted from a carrier of the Atlantic Fleet. Note the four-blade windmills on the nose of the four jamming pods. In a few seconds' time they will be spinning and generating the electrical power needed to pump out the large jamming signals from the front and rear of each pod.**

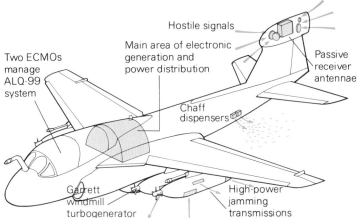

Two ECMOs manage ALQ-99 system

Main area of electronic generation and power distribution

Hostile signals

Passive receiver antennae

Chaff dispensers

Garrett windmill turbogenerator

High-power jamming transmissions

**Above: To make the best use of the available jamming power, the EA-6B receives hostile signals at a battery of passive antennae in the fin cap, giving signal form, wavelength, direction and other information. These data are then used to guide and time the emission of jamming signals so that each jamming radiation is sent out at just the correct time.**

# Ilyushin Il-14

## Il-14 Crate

**Origin:** The OKB named for Sergei V. Ilyushin.
**Type:** ECM/Elint aircraft.
**Powerplant:** Two 1,900hp Shvetsov ASh-82T 18-cylinder engines.
**Dimensions:** Span 104ft (31.69m); length 69ft 11in (21.31m), (14M) 73ft 2in (22.3m); wing area 1,075 sq ft (99.7m²).
**Weights:** Empty (early, typical) 27,557lb (12,500kg), (14M) 27,995lb (12,680kg); payload varies with version from 6,614lb (3,000kg) to 7,275lb (3,300kg); loaded 38,580lb (17,500kg), (14M) 39,683lb (18,000kg).
**Performance:** Maximum speed 268mph (431km/h), (14M) 259mph (417km/h); typical cruising speed 193mph (310km/h); initial climb (14M) 1,220ft (372m)/min; service ceiling (typical) 22,966ft (7km); take-off distance (typical, paved runway) 1,590ft (485m); range (typical, max payload) 250 miles (400km), (typical, max fuel) 1,087 miles (1,750km).
**Armament:** None.
**History:** First flight 1950; service delivery 1954, (ECM/Elint version) 1979.
**Users:** Soviet Union (VVS).

Since 1979 numbers of an ECM/Elint version of the veteran Ilyushin-14 (NATO reporting name: Crate) have been seen in VVS service in East Germany and other Soviet theatres. There are rows of electronic antennae along the top and bottom of the fuselage, and most aircraft feature a large, bulged antenna on the port side of the forward fuselage. The designation and precise role of these ECM/Elint aircraft are not known, but they demonstrate yet again the way in which the Soviets carry on getting value out of old equipment which, in the West, would long since have been disposed of.

The Il-14 airframe was developed over a considerable period in the 1950s and 1960s in an attempt to cure most of the faults and deficiencies of the closely similar Il-12. Even though the new machine was safer and easier to fly, it was, by Western standards, totally uneconomic. A tough, stressed-skin machine, it carried only 18-26 passengers until further extensive modifications were made, increasing capacity to 30-36. Some 3,500 were produced in the USSR and served in very large numbers in the VTA and other branches of the Soviet armed forces, and many still remain in service in second-line units. Some production was also undertaken in East Germany and Czechoslovakia.

**Below: Practically nothing is known in the West about this ECM/Elint version of the veteran Il-14 transport known to NATO as Crate. It appears to have several of the same Elint receivers as the Cub-B version of the much larger An-12 transport, with numerous dorsal blade aerials and ventral hemispherical domes.**

# Ilyushin Il-18

## Il-18 Coot-A

**Origin:** The OKB named for Sergei V. Ilyushin.
**Type:** Multisensor reconnaissance and ECM aircraft.
**Powerplant:** Four 4,250ehp Ivchyenko AI-20M single-shaft turboprops.
**Dimensions:** Span 122ft 8½in (37.4m); length 117ft 9½in (35.9m); height 33ft 4in (10.17m); wing area 1,507 sq ft (140m²).
**Weights:** (18D, typical) empty 77,600lb (35,200kg); maximum payload 29,750lb (13,500kg); maximum take-off 141,095lb (64,000kg).
**Performance:** Maximum cruising speed 419mph (675km/h); normal cruise 388mph (625km/h); typical cruise altitude 25,250–32,800ft (8–10km); take-off distance 4,265ft (1,300m); landing distance 2,790ft (850m); range (max payload, 1hr reserve) 2,300 miles (3,700km), (max fuel, 1hr reserve) 4,040 miles (6,500km).
**Armament:** None.
**History:** First flight 4 July 1957; service delivery 1959, (Coot-A) probably about 1977.
**Users:** Soviet Union.

The Ilyushin-18 (Il-18), originally named Moskva (Moscow), was designed in response to a 1953 Aeroflot specification calling for 75–100 passengers,

**Right: This version of the mass-produced Il-18 turboprop transport is probably the Soviet Union's principal Elint and multisensor recon-naissance aircraft, though the number in service is thought to be quite small. Called Coot-A by NATO, it has a giant pod under the fusel-age which almost certainly houses a large SLAR. Further large pods are mounted on both sides of the forward fuselage. Also visible are the eight other receiver aerials along the underside of the fuselage, but two large blade aerials above the centreline of the forward fuselage are hidden. Coot-A was first seen in 1978 and all the examples so far appear to be painted in VVS or AVMF markings.**

high speed, long range, pressurisation, and the ability to operate from unpaved airstrips. At least 700, and possibly as many as 800, were built, and the Il-18 was the first major Soviet aircraft to find a wide export market. Some dozens were supplied to the Soviet armed forces, mainly the VTA and VVS, principally in the role of VIP and personnel transports, without provision for cargo.

After 1975 surplus civil Il-18s began to be converted to freighters, and a number were also rebuilt as major reconnaissance and ECM platforms; there is also an Elint version. The designation of the ECM variant is not known in the West, but the aircraft is referred to by NATO as Coot-A. The modifications are very extensive and clearly result in a multisensor reconnaissance and stand-off jammer platform of great power and endurance, although one which obviously would not be suitable for accompanying attacking aircraft into hostile airspace. The largest sensor is a Sideways Looking Airborne Radar (SLAR) with a long wavelength transmitter (and therefore of exceptional size), housed in a pod about 33ft 7in (10.25m) long under the forward fuselage. This scans both left and right of the aircraft centreline and, to judge by its dimensions, should have very good discrimination. Two other large fairings, each some 14ft 6in (4.4m) long, are attached along the sides of the forward fuselage, and there is a hatch at the front end which may cover a camera installation. The rest of the fuselage bristles with flush antennae, blade and whip antennae, and small projecting dielectric domes, some of them similar to those mounted on the ECM/Elint version of the Il-14 (*qv*). The Il-18 wing is mounted much further back than on the Il-38 ASW version.

# Mil Mi-4

## Mi-4 Hound-C

**Origin:** The OKB named for Mikhail L. Mil.
**Type:** EW helicopter.
**Powerplant:** One 1,700hp Shvetsov ASh-82V 18-cylinder two-row radial.
**Dimensions:** Diameter of four-blade main rotor 68ft 11in (21m); length of fuselage (ignoring rotors) 55ft 1in (16.8m); overall height 17ft (5.18m).
**Weights:** Empty 11,650lb (5,268kg); maximum loaded 17,200lb (7,800kg).
**Performance:** Economical cruising speed 99mph (160km/h); range 250 miles (400km) with 8 passengers or equivalent, 155 miles (250km) with 11.
**Armament:** None.
**History:** First flight (prototype) 1951, (production) 1952; service delivery 1953; final delivery after 1961.
**Users:** Soviet Union.

Some of the old Mi-4 (NATO reporting name: Hound) helicopters have been converted into EW platforms, carrying powerful tactical jamming, sensing and direction-finding equipment. The VHF band jammers, aimed at NATO combat radio nets, are mounted in the cabin, using very large yagi antenna arrays projecting laterally from the fuselage sides.

Produced in a frantic hurry on Stalin's direct orders, this helicopter looked very like a Sikorsky S-55 when it appeared, but was gradually (and, perhaps, grudgingly) recognised in the West as considerably bigger and more capable than the US S-58, let alone the S-55. Production extended from 1952 well into the 1960s, the estimated total built being some 3,500.

Above: This Comint (communications intelligence) and jamming version of the Mi-4 was first identified in 1977, and given the reporting name Hound-C. Quite large numbers are in use, and in any European land battle they could prove extremely effective in disrupting most NATO communications, other than the latest types using FH (frequency hopping) spread-spectrum techniques. It is curious that, though there have been several studies of the problem, the NATO nations have not a single aircraft in this class (the EH-60A may be bought).

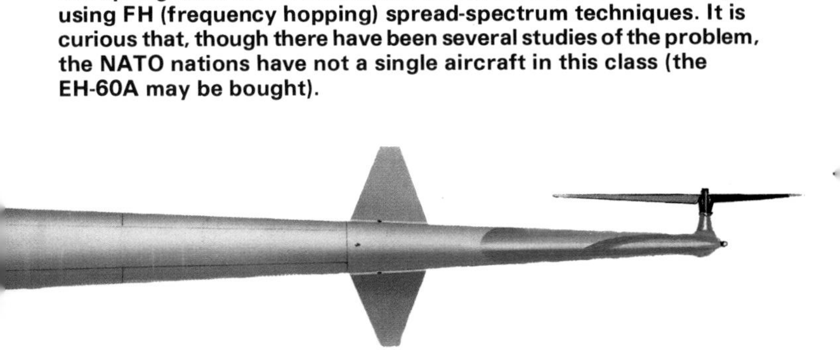

Left: This illustration shows the configuration of the main aerials (antennae) thought to be carried by the Hound-C helicopter. Effective radiated power is limited by the on-board generating capacity, but the five pairs of dipole emitters, each of a different length, are designed to cover all transmissions in five frequency bands. Probably the installation has now been refined to blanket the exact frequencies of the most important NATO radio nets.

# Sikorsky EH-60

## EH-60A

**Origin:** Sikorsky Aircraft Division of United Technologies Corporation, Stratford, Connecticut, USA.
**Type:** EW helicopter.
**Powerplant:** Two 1,560shp General Electric T700-700 free-turbine turboshafts.
**Dimensions:** Diameter of four-blade rotor 53ft 8in (16.36m); overall length (rotors turning) 64ft 10in (19.76m), (rotors/tail folded) 41ft 4in (12.6m); overall height 16ft 10in (5.13m).
**Weights:** Empty 10,624lb (4,819kg); maximum loaded 20,250lb (9,185kg); normal mission weight 16,260lb (7,375kg).
**Performance:** Maximum speed 184mph (296km/h); cruising speed 167mph (269km/h); range (max weight, 30min reserves) 373 miles (600km).
**Armament:** None.
**History:** First flight (YUH) 17 October 1974, (production UH) October 1978, (YEH-60A) 24 September 1981.
**Users:** USA (Army).

The UH-60 was selected in December 1976 after four years of competition with Boeing Vertol for the Utility Tactical Transport Aircraft System (UTTAS) for the US Army. Designed to carry a squad of 11 equipped

infantrymen and a crew of three, the UH-60 can also carry four litters or an external cargo load of 8,000lb (3,628kg).

The EH-60A is an ECM version mounting the Quick Fix II ECM system, together with radar warning augmentation, chaff/flare dispensers and an infra-red jammer. Primary equipment is the ALQ-151 EW system which provides direction-finding (DF), intercept and jamming facilities in the 2–76 MHz frequency range, i.e. it is aimed at Warsaw Pact battlefield tactical communications. External features include four dipole antennae on the rear fuselage and a retractable whip antenna beneath the fuselage. The equipment is operated by a crew of two in the aircraft and can interface, via secure communications links, with any other US Army aircraft similarly equipped, for example the RU-21 and EH-1H; such aircraft would operate in groups of two or three to optimise DF performance. There is also a secure, real-time downlink to the Divisional Tactical Operations Center. Delivery commences in 1984, and a total of 77 EH-60As are expected to be ordered by the US Army.

Another electronic version of the UH-60—the EH-60B—was ordered under the Stand-Off Target Acquisition System (SOTAS) programme, but this was cancelled in 1981 after a prototype had flown.

**Below: Future communications jamming platform of the US Army for over-the-battlefield use, the EH-60A will cost far more—perhaps 100 times more—than the ancient modified Mi-4 Hound helicopters used for this role by the Soviet Union. Capability, however, ought to be considerably greater, though details have not been disclosed. This YEH-60A development aircraft has two pairs of left/ right dipole aerials on the rear fuselage and a large ventral aerial.**

# Tupolev Tu-16

## Tu-16 Badger-A, D, F, H, J, K

**Origin:** The OKB named for Andrei N. Tupolev.
**Type:** ECM/Elint aircraft.
**Powerplant:** Two 20,950lb (9,500kg) thrust Mikulin RD-3M turbojets.
**Dimensions:** Span 109ft 11in (33.5m); length 114ft 2in (34.8m), (D) 120ft 9in (36.8m); height 35ft 5in (10.8m); wing area 1,819 sq ft (169m²).
**Weights:** Empty 92,590lb (42,000kg); maximum loaded 169,755lb (77,000kg).
**Performance:** Maximum speed (typical variant) 587mph (945km/h) at 30,000ft (9km) and above; long-range cruise 485mph (780km/h); service ceiling (typical) 42,650ft (13km); range (typical, max fuel) 3,980 miles (6,400km).
**Armament:** Seven NR-23 cannon in three twin barbettes with one fixed firing ahead.
**History:** First flight 1952; service entry 1955.
**Users:** Soviet Union (VVS, AV-MF).

One of the largest twin-engined bombers ever built, this aircraft, with the OKB designation Tupolev Tu-88, began life as a gravity-bomb strategic bomber. It was later developed as a platform for cruise missiles of various kinds, but, in addition, the ten known variants include dedicated reconnaissance, maritime patrol, ECM and Elint configurations, all using the same basic airframe and systems.

The Badger-D, still on the inventory, is a maritime surveillance and missile-guidance platform with a nose radar, an enlarged chin radar and three ventral antenna fairings for Elint gathering. The F version is an Elint model based on the E but with added receiver pods on wing pylons.

Badger-H is a strategic ECM/ESM aircraft, believed to be used primarily for dispensing large volumes of chaff cut to length aboard the aircraft according to signals received from hostile emitters. There is one teardrop

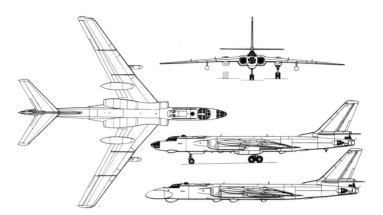

**Above: Three-view of Badger-F with lower side elevation of Badger-D.**

**Below: Badger-K specialised Elint version with very clean exterior broken mainly by small teardrop blisters serving receivers installed in the former weapons bay.**

radome in front of the weapons bay, with a second (plus two blade antennae) behind it. This version may well be the Soviet equivalent of the US EA-6B and EF-111A, intended to escort other aircraft to create electronic "corridors".

The Badger-J (there was no I variant) carries high-powered jammers, with the main generating and transmitting system in a canoe-shaped belly radome. Badger-K is another Elint variant, again with front and rear ventral blisters.

Altogether, the Soviet Air Force has some 90 ECM/Elint Badgers and the Soviet Navy about 40. They are used for regular missions over NATO fleets and along Western European coastlines.

**Left: One of the first Badger-D aircraft was this example seen by US Navy aircraft over the Pacific in January 1963.**

**Below: Standard Badger-D.**

# AEW, AWACS and Command Posts

The concept of an aircraft serving as a platform from which a master observer could control the activities of others goes back to 1916—if not to Capt Coutelle in 1794 (see Introduction). By 1942 the RAF had begun to perfect the techniques of pathfinding and of using a master bomber to direct the main force attack, and of course for generations the ability of the high-flying observer to see more of the whole scene has been useful in assisting commanders on the ground. It is only in recent years that various avionic (aviation electronic) devices have led to new classes of aircraft which carry no normal weapons yet can alter the course of a battle or the course of a war.

The need for early warning of the arrival of hostile aircraft has long been appreciated, but it has seldom been so dramatically or so publicly demonstrated as in the Falklands War of 1982. In that war the Argentine aircraft were able to approach at very low level and high speed, and their first victim was a destroyer deployed as a radar picket to protect the British fleet from such a threat. Ironically, navies had understood this problem much earlier than land-based air forces and for a long time airborne early warning (AEW) was a virtual naval monopoly, with the US Navy and Royal Navy leading the field.

By 1945 the US Navy had the first 36 AEW (airborne early warning) aircraft in service, carrying large and powerful surveillance radars theoretically able to spot even low-flying aircraft close to the ground (which in most radars reflects so much energy as to swamp any return from the target aircraft). AEW radars have got progressively better, and today giant sets are in use, able to operate in many different modes to give clear and infor-mation-packed pictures out to a distance of 230 miles (370km). In some modes they can pick out moving targets against a stationary background, without being misled by violently shaken leaves in a gale or spume blown from the tops of the moving waves. Some radars rotate under the fuselage, some on pylons above the fuselage, but the best answer appears to be an aerial (antenna) at both nose and tail, each covering 180° and with absolutely nothing to interfere with transmission and reception.

Associated with such a radar must be a large digital computer with something like a million words of memory and a central processor with a speed approaching a million operations per second. Another essential is a giant IFF (Identification Friend or Foe) system so linked with the radar that every target can be positively identified as friendly or otherwise (in war, "other-wise" is taken to mean hostile). The aircraft has to have the most reliable and precise navigation systems possible, as well as multiple display stations at which a human crew can study the changing situation on land, sea and in the air. Not least, comprehensive, secure, un-jammable communications links are needed to commanders on the surface or in other aircraft.

Assembling these devices can turn yesterday's AEW aircraft into today's AWACS, a term first applied to the E-3A Sentry but preceded in time by the US Navy's E-1 Tracer and E-2 Hawkeye. Such aircraft can warn of the approach of enemy attack aircraft, warn friendly attack aircraft of hostile interceptors or give them the best updated course to steer to avoid defences or find a hostile ship, and can even assist and direct a land or sea battle. These complex machines are in-evitably very expensive, and only

**Above: This prototype, designated the Boeing EC-137D, was the chief ancestor of today's growing fleets of highly capable AWACS aircraft. Superficially it resembled today's E-3A and E-3B Sentries.**

the largest air forces can afford AWACS fleets of their own. The threat has, however, been sufficiently serious to compel NATO nations to get together jointly to procure and operate a fleet of E-3As, an unprecedented step in an otherwise very individualistic alliance.

Finally in this field are the command posts, of which the E-4 and versions of the EC-135 are the most important to date. These aircraft have no comparable radar, but they mount comprehensive communications systems, enabling them to control the deployment and use of deterrent forces. Relays of such aircraft provide a continuous and survivable command system, with flight endurance extended by inflight refuelling; indeed, the main limitation seems to be the supply of engine oil! The USSR is also producing aircraft of this type — mainly Antonov An-12s — and recently completed a major national exercise based on their use.

The reasoning behind the airborne command post is that deterrent forces have to be survivable, and be seen to be so. There is no point in having large forces of ICBMs (intercontinental ballistic missiles) in nuclear-hardened silos deep in the earth if a single enemy warhead knocks out the head of state or national command authority. There are not many economically viable answers to this particular problem, but one is to carry the national command structure aloft inside a large aircraft equipped with exceptional communications systems. The weak link in the chain is that an actual nuclear attack would probably be mounted without the courtesy of a prior warning, so the AABNCP (advanced airborne command post) would still be on the ground on standby.

As is the case with all branches of military operations, we know all about the US hardware and philosophy and relatively little about the corresponding Soviet operation. Boeing and the USAF have created a fantastic flying machine in the E-4B, capable of providing a safe nuclear-proof base for 60+ people.

# Boeing E-3 Sentry and E-6 TACAMO

## E-3A, E-6A

**Origin:** Boeing Aerospace Company, Kent, Washington.
**Type:** Airborne Warning and Control System (AWACS) platform.
**Powerplant:** Four 21,000lb (9,526kg) thrust Pratt & Whitney TF331-100/100A turbofans.
**Dimensions:** Span 145ft 9in (44.42m); length 152ft 11in (46.61m); height 41ft 4in (12.6m) over fin; wing area 3,050 sq ft (283.4m$^2$).
**Weights:** Empty about 162,000lb (73,480kg); loaded 325,000lb (147,400kg).
**Performance:** Maximum speed 530mph (853km/h); normal operating speed about 350mph (563km/h); service ceiling over 29,000ft (8.85km); endurance on station (1,000 miles, 1,609km, from base) 6hrs.
**Armament:** None.
**History:** First flight (EC-137D) 5 February 1972, (E-3A) 31 October 1975; USAF service delivery (E-3A) 24 March 1977, NATO service delivery (E-3A) 22 January 1982.
**Users:** (E-3) USA (Air Force), NATO, Saudi Arabia; (E-6) USA (Navy).

The USAF has been one of the pioneers of overland surveillance platforms, starting with the EC-121 Warning Star, which was based on the Super Constellation and continued in unpublicised service until 1980. During the 1960s radar technology reached the point at which, with

**Below: Perhaps surprisingly, the USAF's E-3A Sentry aircraft are operated not by SAC but by TAC, whose blue, red and gold badge is displayed on each of these grey-painted machines. The other badge is that of the 552nd AWAC Wing, whose home base is Tinker AFB. In this photograph the air-refuelling doors are open.**

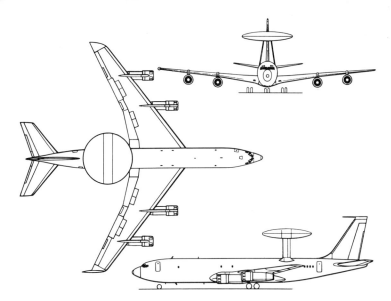

**Above: Three-view of E-3A Sentry with early engine inlets.**

greater power and rapid digital processing, an over-the-horizon (OTH) capability could be achieved, plus clear vision looking almost straight down to detect and track high-speed aircraft flying at low-level. A vital element was the pulse-doppler radar, in which the "doppler-shift" in received frequency caused by relative motion between the target and the radar platform can be used to separate out all unwanted reflections. Sophisticated signal processing is needed to eliminate returns from such false "moving targets" as leaves violently disturbed by the wind, and, most difficult of all, the motion of the sea and of blown spray in an oceanic gale.
▶

Left: TAC aircrew, highly qualified for their responsible role, working at MPCs (multi-purpose consoles) in an E-3A during a training mission. Such flights take place over large geographical areas, and special AWAC support squadrons have been established in Iceland, Alaska and Okinawa. Other E-3A missions have been based from Saudi Arabia and Egypt.

► While Hughes and Westinghouse fought to develop the new Overland Downlook Radar (ODR), Boeing was awarded a prime contract on 8 July 1970 for the Airborne Warning and Control System (AWACS). Their proposal was based on the commercial 707-320 airliner, but, to give enhanced on-station endurance, the aircraft was to be powered by eight TF34 engines; this was later changed back to the original four engines, but each driving a high-power generator. The antenna for the main radar, back-to-back with identification friend or foe (IFF) and communications antennae, is mounted on two 11ft (3.35m) struts above the rear fuselage and streamlined by adding two D-shaped radomes of glassfibre sandwich which turn the girder-like antenna array into a deep circular rotodome some 30ft (9.14m) in diameter and 6ft (1.83m) deep. The rotating mass weighs 3,395lb (1,540kg) and the rotodome itself is angled 2.5° downwards to minimise aerodynamic moments on the turntable. The rotodome turns very slowly to keep the bearings lubricated; when on station it rotates at 6rpm (once every 10 seconds) and the searchlight-like beam is electronically scanned in elevation under computer control (azimuth scan is achieved by the rotation of the rotodome). The rival radars were flown in two EC-137D aircraft, and the winning Westinghouse APY-1 radar was built into the first E-3A in 1975.

The first E-3A force was built up in Tactical Air Command (TAC) to support quick-reaction deployment and tactical operations by all TAC units. The 552nd AWAC Wing received its first E-3A at Tinker AFB, Oklahoma, on 24 March 1977 and went on operational duty a year later; subsequently, the 552nd has operated in many parts of the world. It was augmented from 1979 by NORAD (North American Air Defense) personnel whose mission is the surveillance of all North American airspace and control of NORAD assets over the continental USA.

From the 22nd aircraft, an overwater capability has been incorporated, and from No 24 the systems are upgraded with links into the Joint Tactical Information Distribution System (JTIDS) shared by all NATO forces. The planned USAF force is 46 aircraft, funded at two per year.

Since the provision of national airborne early warning fleets was clearly too expensive for most of the NATO allies, plans were drawn up in the

**Above: This aircraft, the first of 18 funded and operated by NATO European nations, is actually registered to the Duchy of Luxembourg.**

**Below: Predecessor of the E-3A, the Boeing EC-137D tested the radar.**

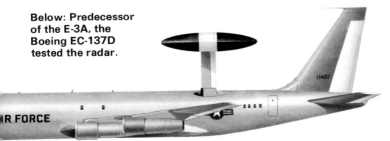

late 1970s for a multinational force of 18 aircraft. These needed a degree of maritime surveillance capability, so Westinghouse began work on this in 1976 under a USAF contract. NATO also specified additional HF radio communications and a radio teletype for maritime use, an IDS tactical communications system, new data-processing equipment based on the IBM System 4Pi Model CC-2 computer, and underwing hardpoints for defensive systems.

The new computer has a memory capacity of more than 665,000 words—more than five times that of the earlier CC-1 model for the USAF—and can carry out 1.25 million operations per second. This gives the NATO-standard E-3A great data-processing speed and capacity, as well as the ability to initiate target tracks automatically. The official designation of the updated radar is APY-2.

Five basic operating modes are possible, and the APY-2 can, like the 1, change its operating mode from scan to scan, or even from one part of a scan to another. For maximum long-range performance, a low-PRF beyond-the-horizon mode may be used, but if good range resolution is required, the shorter range, pulse-doppler, non-elevation scan is used. In order to obtain elevation data the radar can be operated in pulse-doppler elevation scan mode, but this causes a further deterioration in range. Targets radiating radar energy may be tracked by means of a passive mode, in which the radar acts as a receiver and thus does not betray its presence to the target.

In the maritime mode, the threshold of the moving-target indication circuitry is reduced from 80kt (148km/h) to zero, so that slow-moving or even stationary surface targets are displayed. A very short pulse is used in this mode, reducing the amount of sea clutter in the return signal.

On normal patrol the E-3A cruises at Mach 0.72 at an altitude of 29,000ft (8.8km); under these conditions the radar has a range of just over 230 miles (368km) against low-level targets. The E-3A can remain on patrol for 9 to 11 hours, but this can be extended to 22 hours by inflight refuelling; however, whilst both the USAF and Saudi Air Force will be supported by tankers, the NATO E-3A force will not.

There are plans to fit USAF and NATO E-3As with ECM systems, and ▶

▶ there are hardpoints on the NATO aircraft suitable for chaff dispensers, while mountings and cabling have been fitted into the wing-roots and leading edges to accommodate future ECM equipment and antennae.

The other customer to date is the Royal Saudi Air Force, but in this case the system will be slightly downgraded by the removal of highly classified equipment such as JTIDS. The planned fleet of five E-3As will give a better air defence capability than would be possible with a network of 48 ground-based radars. The aircraft are due to enter service in 1986, and will be based initially at Dharhan, later moving to a new airfield at Kharji.

Current orders for the E-3A are 34 for the USAF (with funding requested for another 12 in the years 1985–88); 18 for NATO; and five for Saudi Arabia. There remains a possibility that France may order "a few", although this would have to await an improvement in that country's economic situation.

Yet another version of the long-lived Boeing 707/C-135 design was recently announced when Boeing won an order for the replacement

aircraft for the TACAMO mission (which is described in more detail under the Lockheed C-130 entry). The new aircraft, designated E-6A, is a rebuilt ex-airline 707 and is to be powered by four GE/SNECMA CFM56 turbofans, which also power the re-engined KC-135R. Fifteen EC-6As are to be procured, at a cost of $1,600 million, and they will be fitted with special mission-related electronics. They will be EMP-hardened as befits their role in communicating to SSBNs before, during and after a nuclear first-strike, and will carry an ESM system. The aircraft will have a range of some 6,900 miles (11,200km) but will also have inflight-refuelling equipment.

**Below: One of the best-looking of the seemingly limitless military Boeing 707 variants, the TACAMO E-6A costs something like $100 million each. VLF trailing antennas are among equipment in the wing-tip pods, and communications systems will be capable of secure links with submerged submarines.**

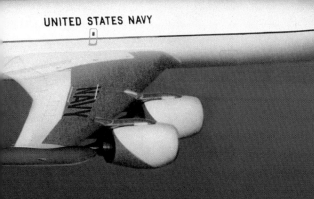

# Boeing E-4 NEACP

## E-4B

**Origin:** Boeing Aerospace Company, Kent, Washington.
**Type:** National emergency airborne command post.
**Powerplant:** Four 52,500lb (23,814kg) thrust General Electric F103 (CF6-50E) turbofans.
**Dimensions:** Span 195ft 8in (59.64m); length 231ft 10in (70.66m); wing area 5,500 sq ft (511m²).
**Weights:** Empty about 410,000lb (186,000kg); loaded 803,000lb (364,241kg).
**Performance:** Maximum speed 602mph (969km/h) at 700,000lb (317,515kg) at 30,000ft (9.14km); typical cruising speed 583mph (939km/h) at 35,000ft (10.67km); maximum range (full tanks) 7,100 miles (11,426km); take-off field length (ISA) 10,400ft (3,170m); cruise ceiling 45,000ft (13.12km).
**Armament:** None.
**History:** First flight (747 prototype) 9 February 1969, (E-4A) 13 June 1973, (E-4B) 10 June 1978.
**Users:** USA.

▶

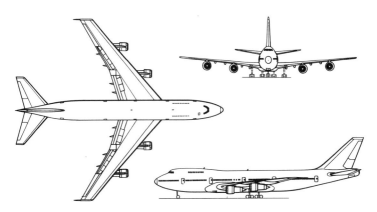

Above: Three-view of commercial Boeing 747 with JT9D engines.

Below: Though powered by General Electric F103 (CF6-50E) engines, which replaced those originally fitted at no cost to the USAF, this aircraft is an E-4A which has now been brought up to E-4B standard.

▶ This unique variant of the commercial 747 transport is being procured in small numbers to supplement the various EC-135 airborne command posts of the US National Military Command System and SAC. Under the 481B NEACP (National Emergency Airborne Command Post) programme, the Air Force Electronic Systems Division awarded Boeing a contract in February 1973 for two unequipped aircraft, designated E-4A and powered by JT9D engines, to which a third aircraft was added in July 1973. E-Systems won the contract to instal interim equipment in these three E-4A aircraft, the first of which was delivered to Andrews AFB in December 1974. The next two were delivered in 1975, the third differing in being powered by the GE F103 engine (made standard and subsequently retrofitted to the first two aircraft).

In December 1973 a fourth aircraft was contracted for, and this was fitted with more advanced equipment, resulting in the designation E-4B. All E-4As have been brought up to the same standard and are also designated E-4B. The first E-4B (75-0125) was delivered on 21 December 1979. The E-4B has accommodation for a larger battle staff on its 4,620 sq ft (429.2m²) main deck, which is divided into five operating areas: the National Command Authorities area, the conference room, the briefing room, the battle staff compartment and the communications control centre. The flight deck includes a special navigation station not normally found in 747s and a crew rest area, essential for missions which, with inflight refuelling, can last up to 72 hours. The flight crew consists of captain, co-pilot, navigator and flight engineer; the battle staff comprises force status controllers (3), enemy

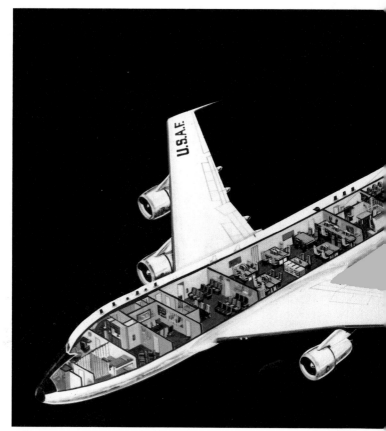

action NCO, operations controller, communications controller, intelligence planners (4), operations planners (4), logistics planners (4), chief of battle staff, airborne launch system officers (2), weather officer, reconnaissance planner, damage assessment officer and administrators (2), a total of 26; and communications staff include radio operators (3), record communications operators (5), radio maintenance men (5) and switchboard operators (2), a total of 15. The Looking Glass mission (described more fully in the EC-135 entry) is commanded by a general officer with two staff officers, while the NEACP role takes an undisclosed number more. There are thus at least 48 personnel aboard on any mission.  ▶

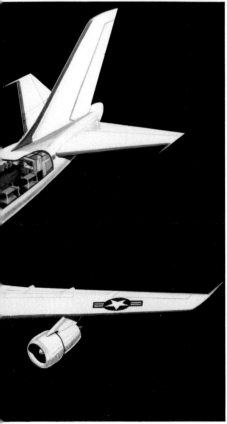

**Above: No other aircraft built in quantity is believed to cost as much as the E-4B, whose installations are on a giant scale and in many respects unique. This shows the communications control centre, one of the most costly and comprehensive of its kind.**

**Left: Simplified cutaway of an E-4B showing the main working areas for the USA's National Command Authority (which includes the US President and the Commander of SAC, both of whom would fly on board in a crisis), the briefing and rest rooms and the complex communications centre, served by the most powerful of all airborne radio installations, mainly under the main floor. The E-4B, as now in service, adds a doghouse installation above the fuselage (see next page) for an SHF receiver/ transmit system.**

**Above: US Air Force aircraft number 75-0125 is the same as that pictured previously, but here it is brought up to current E-4B standard with the SHF doghouse installation. Studies are even in hand to adapt the airframe of the 747-300, with an increased-capacity upper deck, for a later version of the E-4.**

The E-4 staff is tasked with strategic command and decision-making, acting as a survivable back-up to ground-based facilities which are likely to be very early targets in a nuclear conflict. To fulfil this role, the E-4 has an extensive array of data-processing and communications equipment.

The aircraft's equipment includes new SHF radios capable of interfacing with military communications satellites in the Defense Satellite Communications System (DSCS-2) network. The 33in (83.82cm) computer-controlled dish for this is located in a dorsal fairing, not present on the earlier E-4A. The E-4B can communicate with the ground over a wide range of frequencies covering virtually the entire radio communications spectrum from 14kHz to 8.4GHz. Fourteen ground stations can handle traffic from the E-4B, linking it into the main US ground-based communications networks.

Each aircraft is fitted with a retractable LF/VHF wire antenna some 5,000ft (1,524m) long, which is used by up to 13 communications links. Much attention has been given to hardening the communications and avionics against electro-magnetic pulse (EMP)—effects produced by nuclear explosions—especially as the trailing wire antenna, so essential for communicating with ballistic missile submarines, is also particularly effective in picking up EMP!

The E-4B force will probably be fitted with equipment capable of receiving data directly from Defense Support Programme early-warning and attack assessment satellites. An improved Airborne Launch Control System (ALCS) may also be fitted, allowing the NEACP to re-target Minuteman and Peacekeeper (formerly MX) ICBMs; the existing ALCS allows Minuteman missiles to be launched on command from the E-4B, but not re-targeted. The launch codes are carried in volatile memory units which are physically destroyed by an automatic system if power is removed for more than three minutes, in order to guard against their being compromised in the event of an E-4 crash.

There are six E-4Bs, all currently based at Offutt Air Force Base in Nebraska.

# Hawker Siddeley (Avro) Shackleton

## Shackleton AEW Mk 2

**Origin:** A.V. Roe Ltd (now BAe), UK.
**Type:** Airborne Early Warning aircraft.
**Powerplant:** Four 2,455hp Rolls-Royce Griffon 57A V-12 liquid cooled engines.
**Dimensions:** Span 120ft (36.58m); length 87ft 3in (26.59m); height 16ft 9in (5.1m); wing area 1,451 sq ft (134.8m²).
**Weights:** Maximum take-off 108,000lb (49,000kg).
**Performance:** Maximum speed 298mph (480km/h); service ceiling 20,000ft (6.1km); endurance 18hr; range 2,900 miles (4,665km).
**Armament:** None.
**History:** First flight (MR Mk 1) 9 March 1949; (AEW Mk 2) 1971-72.
**Users:** UK (RAF).

The Shackleton AEW Mk 2 can trace its lineage back to the Avro Manchester twin-engined bomber, which first flew in 1939. Somewhat underpowered, the Manchester was given four Rolls-Royce Merlin engines and became the immortal Lancaster, which in turn was developed into the Lincoln. There had been several maritime reconnaissance versions of the Lancaster, but the aircraft which started life as the Lincoln ASR Mk 3 was sufficiently different to be renamed the Shackleton MR Mk 1; this, too, was developed through Mk 2 to Mk 3, which entered service in 1957 and was eventually replaced by the Nimrod in 1969.

In the late 1960s, however, the threat to the UK from low-level aircraft flying under the radar became apparent, and the Air Staff stated an urgent,

**Above: The Shackleton AEW.2 is the final example of a family of aircraft which began in 1936 and included the Lancaster, parts of whose wing structure are common to the aircraft still in use. The final maritime-patrol variant was the Mk 3B, but the older Mk 2, with a tailwheel, was selected for rebuilding as the RAF's first dedicated AEW platform in the first half of the 1960s.**

**Right: A Shackleton AEW.2 in the circuit at RAF Lossiemouth, the contra-rotating propellers being discernible. By a wide margin, this is the last large piston-engined aircraft in British service. The actual radars fitted to these machines are advanced developments of the original American APS-20 built in Britain, and they are certainly not the same sets as were fitted to the AD-4W Skyraiders.**

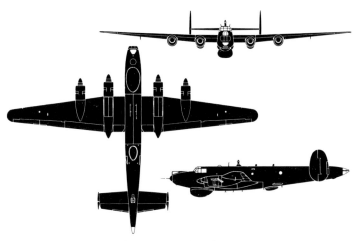

**Above: Three-view of Shackleton AEW.2.**

if somewhat belated, requirement for an airborne early warning aircraft. The only suitable airframes available were some Shackleton Mk 2s in storage, and the only radar was the APS-20B, which had seen service in carrier-borne Fleet Air Arm Fairey Gannet AEW aircraft. Twelve Shackleton AEW Mk 2s were produced, all of them serving with 8 Squadron at RAF Lossiemouth. Nobody can pretend that this was anything more than the proverbial "lash up", and the RAF will doubtless be profoundly thankful when the Nimrod AEW Mk 3 (*qv*) enters service in 1984. Nevertheless, the Shackleton AEW Mk 2 has filled a vital gap for over a decade, one regret being their inability (through lack of inflight refuelling) to give cover over the Falklands during the 1982 war.

# BAe Nimrod

## Nimrod AEW Mk 3, R Mk 1

**Origin:** British Aerospace, UK.
**Type:** (AEW Mk 3) airborne early warning aircraft; (R Mk 1) strategic electronic reconnaissance aircraft.
**Powerplant:** Four 12,140lb (5,520kg) Rolls-Royce Spey 250 turbofans.
**Dimensions:** Span 115ft 1in (35.08m); length 137ft 9in (41.97m); height 35ft (10.67m); wing area 2,121 sq ft (197m²).
**Weights:** Not disclosed.
**Performance:** Maximum speed 575mph (926km/h); typical patrol speed 230mph (370km/h); typical endurance 10+ hrs.
**Armament:** None.
**History:** First flight (Nimrod MR Mk 1) 28 June 1968, (Nimrod AEW Mk 3) 16 July 1980.
**Users:** UK (RAF).

In the search for a replacement for the piston-engined Shackleton MR.3, the Royal Air Force considered many designs ranging from derivatives of the CL-44 and of the Trident airliner to a four-engined Mach 2 variable-geometry aircraft. The final requirement was virtually written around the Breguet Atlantic, but Hawker Siddeley hastily prepared the HS.801 design to combine the wings and fuselage of the Comet airliner with the Rolls-Royce Spey 250 powerplant. An unpressurised ventral section was added to the fuselage in order to create the internal volume for a large weapons bay. A total of 46 production Nimrod maritime reconnaissance aircraft were ordered by the RAF, and deliveries began in 1969. Only five of the final batch of eight Nimrods were delivered as MR.1s; one became the prototype MR.2, while the remaining two became prototypes for the AEW Mk 3.

By 1977 the RAF was becoming desperate for a replacement for the Shackleton AEW Mk 2 (*qv*) and there was increasing disenchantment with the protracted delays affecting NATO's plans for an E-3A force, and so the British Government took the decision to "go it alone" with an early warning version of the Nimrod, a decision which was very welcome for the British avionics industry since the resulting programme includes the most complex avionics equipment ever fitted to a front-line RAF aircraft. Original plans called for the system to be operational by 1982, but this date slipped first

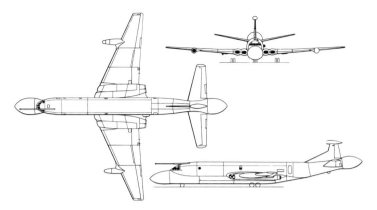

**Above: Three-view of the Nimrod AEW.3 showing the inflight-refuelling probe but omitting the wing-tip ESM aerial pods.**

to 1983 and then to 1984. Some consideration has been given to changing the aircraft's name in recognition of its new mission, but for the moment it remains the Nimrod AEW Mk 3.

A total of eleven AEW Mk 3 aircraft are being built, using Nimrod airframes originally manufactured for maritime patrol use. Twin antenna assemblies for the Marconi Avionics search radar and Cossor Jubilee-Guardsman IFF are mounted in the nose and tail radomes, each covering 180° in azimuth. Each covers 180° sequentially with the other, thus giving 360° coverage and avoiding the aerodynamic and radar obscuration problems inherent in rotodomes. The strucutral changes affect aircraft performance only slightly, and directional stability is maintained by a 3ft (0.91m) increase in the height of the fin. Despite its size, the nose radome does not interfere with the forward view of the pilot during take-off and landing. A Loral ESM system is mounted in the wing-tip pods, which detects and analyses radio and radar transmissions. ▶

**Below: Following tests of the nose-hemisphere radar and communications in a rebuilt Comet in 1977, the first of three AEW.3 development aircraft, XZ286, flew in July 1980. It was painted in the original white/grey livery, later superseded by the colour called hemp.**

▶ The radar is optimised for use over water, so forming a good operating partner for the APY-1 radar of the Boeing E-3A since the latter is designed for over-land use. As a result, the combined fleet of Nimrod AEW Mk 3 and E-3A aircraft available to NATO will give the Alliance better warning facilities than would have been possible with a single type. The two types will also be able to intercommunicate, initially using the NATO Link 11 system and later JTIDS spread-spectrum equipment.

The first production AEW Mk 3 made its maiden flight on 9 March 1982 and was to be delivered in mid-1983. The aircraft should become operational with 8 Squadron in 1984 at RAF Waddington.

Another specialised version of the Nimrod is the R Mk 1. This is used in the electronic intelligence (Elint) role, and three aircraft (additional to the 46 production MR Mk 1s) are operated by 51 Squadron at RAF Wyton. The major recognition feature of this highly classified aircraft is the deletion of the MAD tailboom and the addition of three receiving antennae (one on the tailcone and the others facing forward on the wing tanks).

**Below: XZ285, the first production Nimrod AEW.3, made its first flight on 9 March 1982. The colour scheme, grey and so-called hemp, is now standard for all Royal Air Force Nimrods and is also applied to other large aircraft.**

Above: One of the three Nimrod R.1 Elint aircraft, which are immediately distinguished from the maritime patrol version by their three passive receiver installations, one each on the noses of the wing pods and the third on the tail (replacing the MAD boom).

# Grumman E-2 Hawkeye

## E-2C

**Origin:** Grumman Aerospace Corporation, Bethpage, NY.
**Type:** Carrier-and land-based airborne early warning and control (AWACS) platform.
**Powerplant:** Two 4,910ehp (3,660ekW) T56-A-425 Allison turboprops.
**Dimensions:** Span 80ft 7in (24.56m); length 57ft 6¾in (17.54m); height 18ft 3¾in (5.58m); wing area 700 sq ft (65.03m²).
**Weights:** Empty 37,945lb (17,211kg); maximum take-off 51,817lb (23,503kg).
**Performance:** Maximum speed 374mph (602km/h); maximum cruising speed 365mph (587km/h); normal cruising speed 310mph (500km/h); service ceiling 30,800ft (9.39km); endurance (max fuel) 6hr 6min.
**Armament:** None.
**History:** First flight (E-2) 21 October 1960, (E-2C) 20 January 1971; first delivery (E-2A) 19 January 1964.
**Users:** USA (Navy), Israel, Japan, Singapore, Egypt.

Since 1975 there has been an intensification of interest in AEW and AWACS type platforms, following belated recognition of the fact that they can greatly enhance the effectiveness of an air force and also be of considerable assistance to the operations of naval and ground forces. Major land-based aircraft of this type (E-3A, Nimrod, Tu-126) are beyond the practical means of most air forces in terms of both costs and manpower. The compact E-2 Hawkeye, however, was designed to operate from an aircraft carrier and is thus more manageable in all respects. It is also unique in that it is still the only aircraft in the world to be designed specifically for the AEW/AWACS role, unlike others which are conversions of airliners or bombers. It has already been bought or ordered by Israel (4 aircraft), Japan (8), Singapore (4 in 1985) and Egypt (2 in 1984, 2 in 1985); Pakistan and Australia are also known to be interested, and France (currently without any AEW platform in service or on order) has formally evaluated the aircraft.

**Below: Despite severe compromises to fit aircraft carriers, the E-2C is so capable it has sold to a growing number of air forces on land.**

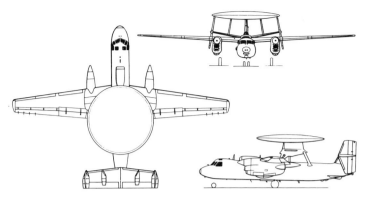

**Above: Three-view of E-2C showing rotodome fully extended.**

**Below: Turboprops were chosen to give the necessary flight performance combined with long endurance on a limited fuel supply, but inevitably cause some interference with radar operation.**

Grumman was the pioneer of sea-going AEW with the AF-2W Guardian, which was followed by the twin-engined E-1B Tracer in which, for the first time, the radar was placed above, rather than below, the fuselage. By the late 1950s, increasing demands led to the design of the W2F predecessor of today's Hawkeye which was, with various sub-types of the EC-121, the first aircraft to have the new style of rotodome in which the antenna itself is given a streamlined fairing instead of being housed inside a radome. The size of airframe needed to house the APS-96 radar was such that considerable ingenuity was needed; for example, four fins and rudders are used, all mounted at 90° to the dihedral tailplane and all well below the wake of the saucer-like rotodome. The rotodome itself is set at a positive incidence in flight to lift at least its own weight, while on the ground it is retracted a short distance to enable it to clear the roof of the hangar on board aircraft carriers.

The dome rotates once every 10 seconds when in operation and the radar gives surveillance from a height of 30,000ft (9.15km) within a radius of 300 miles (480km). Ten years into the programme, the APS-96 was replaced by the much more advanced APS-125 with an Advanced Radar Processing System (ARPS) which gives a much improved discrimination and detection capability over both land and water. With this new radar the aircraft designation changed to E-2C, which model entered service in 1973 and remains the standard "eyes" of the US Navy at sea, with numerous updates in the subsequent years.  ▶

► The two pilots occupy a wide "airline" type flight deck. Behind them, amidst a mass of radar racking and the high-capacity vapour-cycle cooling system (the radiator for which is housed in a large duct above the fuselage), is the pressurised Airborne Tactical Data System (ATDS) compartment. This is the nerve-centre of the aircraft, manned by the combat information officer, air control officer and radar operator. They are presented with displays and outputs not only from the main radar but also from some 30 other electronic devices, including "state of the art" passive detectors and communications systems. These combine to give a picture of targets, tracks and trajectories, and signal emissions, all duly processed and, where appropriate, with IFF interrogation replies. Passive Detection System (PDS) antennae are located on the nose and tail, and on the tips of the tailplane for lateral coverage.

Production of the E-2C is slow but steady, with the 95th airframe due to be delivered in 1987. Its crews are enthusiastic, and Grumman has found them valuable assistants in their successful efforts to sell the aircraft to foreign customers. It would be possible to build a slightly more efficient platform using the same radar and engines if it did not have to meet the requirements for carrier operation. Existing export customers have, however, been happy to take the aircraft as it is; in fact, the Israelis have turned the wing-folding capability to advantage as it has enabled them to park their E-2Cs in fighter-style protected shelters.

**Above: The amazing compactness of the Hawkeye is emphasised by the fact that this photograph shows the entire machine, with wings folded for handy parking.**

**Above: The first export customer was Israel, whose Heyl Ha'Avir (Israel Defence Force/Air Force) paid roughly $160 million to acquire four aircraft. They have been in constant combat use.**

A mission can last up to six hours, and at a radius of 200 miles (322km) the time on station at 30,000ft (9.1km) can be almost 4 hours. This is appreciably shorter than the 10 hours at this radius of the E-3A and Nimrod, but Grumman claim a 2:1 price differential in acquisition and operating costs (the E-2C costs £39 million—$58 million—at 1983 prices). The E-2C radar can detect airborne targets anywhere in a 3,000,000 cubic mile surveillance envelope, and it is claimed that a target as small as a cruise missile can be detected at ranges over 115 miles (185km), fighters at ranges up to 230 miles (370km), and larger aircraft at 289 miles (465km). All friendly and enemy maritime movements can also be monitored. The AN/ALR-59 PDS can detect the presence of electronic emitters at ranges up to twice that of the radar system. High speed data processing enables the E-2C automatically to track more than 250 targets at the same time and to control more than 30 airborne intercepts. A new Total Radiation Aperture Control antenna (TRAC-A) is now under development, and this will enable the range to be increased, reduce the sidelobes and enhance the ECCM capability. It is of interest that development funding, which was some £12.5 million ($18.8 million) in FY82, rose to £35 million ($52.3 million) in FY83, indicating that many more improvements are on the way. Grumman has for many years had a team working on improved Hawkeyes, some with turbofan propulsion, and even on a completely new and very advanced replacement (E-7).

**Left: The Israeli Heyl Ha' Avir put the Hawkeyes into service without painting on any of the usual three-figure service numbers, perhaps indicative of even more than the usual degree of tight security. The black strips along the wings and tail leading edges are pneumatic pulsating rubber de-icers. External stencils are mainly in English, which is unusual.**

# Ilyushin Il-76

## Il-76 SUAWACS

**Origin:** The OKB named for Sergei V. Ilyushin, under General Designer Novozhilov.
**Type:** Airborne Warning and Control System (AWACS) platform.
**Powerplant:** Four 26,455lb (12,00kg) thrust Soloviev D-30KP
**Dimensions:** Span 165ft 8in (50.5m); length 152ft 10½in (46.59m); height 48ft 5in (14.76m); wing area 3,229 sq ft (300m²).
**Weights:** (Basic transport) empty about 176,400lb (80,000kg); maximum payload 88,185lb (40,000kg); maximum loaded 374,785lb (170,000kg).
**Performance:** Maximum speed 528mph (850km/h); cruising speed 466–497mph (750–800km/h); normal cruising altitude 29,500–39,370ft (9–12km); take-off distance (paved runway) 2,790ft (850m), landing distance 1,475ft (450m); range (max payload) 3,100 miles (5,000km); range (max fuel) 4,163 miles (6,700km).
**Armament:** Twin guns (NR-23?) in tail turret.
**History:** First flight 25 March 1971; service delivery (evaluation) believed 1973, (inventory) 1983-84.
**Users:** Soviet Union.

As a result of experience gained with the Tu-126 Moss early warning aircraft, Soviet radar designers felt ready by the mid-1970s to embark on the development of a new generation AWACS platform. Such a move had been widely anticipated by the US intelligence services, which in the latter part of that decade monitored specific areas of Soviet military research and development for the first signs that the necessary technology was emerging from Soviet laboratories. By the end of the 1970s the signs were quite clear. Photographs taken by US reconnaissance satellites show that the basic airframe of the Il-76 Candid turbojet transport has been adapted for the new role by the addition of an AWACS-style radome mounted directly above the wing trailing-edge, with a second, smaller, E-4-style dorsal fairing housing antennae for satellite communications. US intelligence has already obtained Elint data on the radar, allowing the planning of a suitable ECM system to begin. The set operates in the 2.3-2.4GHz area, and waveform analysis shows that the technology used is particularly advanced.

One potential weakness identified by the USAF is that the tall T-tail of the Il-76 may create a slight "blind spot" in azimuth coverage. The full extent of any problem is probably only known to the Soviet Air Force, since the practical effects of such obscuration are difficult to predict. US engineers will doubtless have investigated the phenomenon in laboratory studies, using millimetre wavelengths and carefully prepared scale models of the aircraft. Specific anti-SUAWACS countermeasures have already been studied. The approaches considered include the development of a new version of the Boeing SRAM air-launched missile and the fitting of additional ECM equipment to the B-52H strategic bomber and US cruise missiles.

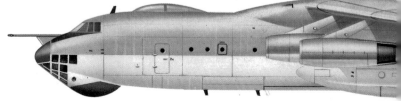

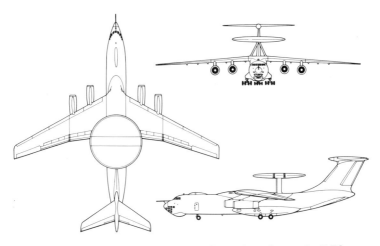

**Above: Still largely speculative, this three-view shows the Il-76 (Candid) variant now believed to be in production as the principal Soviet AWACS aircraft. Features include a US-style rotodome on a braced mast, lengthened forward fuselage and inflight-refuelling probe. It is not known if a rear turret is fitted as in the Il-76M.**

Construction and deployment are expected to be organised as a "crash" programme, with the first aircraft being fielded in 1983-84. The eventual fleet is expected to outnumber the USAF/NATO E-3A force, with at least 50 aircraft being operational by 1985-86. Some sources have suggested that the Soviet's long-term plan may be to use the Il-86 Camber wide-bodied airliner as the basis for the definitive SUAWACS, and that the Il-76 is merely an interim programme resulting from the well-publicised delays to the Il-86. Only time will tell whether this is correct or not.

Superficially, this Ilyushin design resembles the Lockheed C-141, but the general specification resembles that of the USAF's erstwhile C-X. Its 3,100-mile (5,000km) range is likely to be extended by inflight refuelling. Despite the stories about the use of Il-86, the Il-76 appears to be a sensible airframe to use as the basis for an AWACS. The large numbers predicted to be ordered are intended to give coverage of the vast land area of the USSR, although some may well be deployed abroad to meet specific crises, as have USAF E-3As (e.g. to Saudi Arabia), though it is very unlikely that there will be an AWACS version of the Il-86.

**Below: Another speculative representation of the so-called "SUAWACS".**

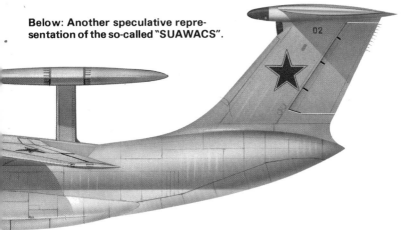

# Lockheed EC-130 Hercules

## EC-130E, MC-130E, EC-130G, EC-130H, EC-130Q, EC-130ARE

**Origin:** Lockheed-Georgia Company, Marietta, Georgia.

**Type:** Originally multirole airlift transport; for special variants see text.

**Powerplant:** For Allison T56 turboprops, (B and E families) 4,050ehp T56-7, (H family) 4,910ehp T56-15 flat-rated at 4,508ehp.

**Dimensions:** Span 132ft 7in (40.41m); length 97ft 9in (29.79m); wing area 1,745 sq ft (162.12m²).

**Weights:** Empty (basic E, H) 72,892lb (33,063kg); operating weight (H) 75,832lb (34,397kg); loaded (E, H) 155,000lb (70,310kg); maximum overload 175,000lb (79,380kg).

**Performance:** Maximum speed/maximum cruising speed 386mph (621km/h) at 175,000lb (79,380kg); economical cruise 345mph (556km/h); initial .SL climb (E) 1,830ft (558m)/min, (H) 1,900ft (579m)/min; service ceiling (E) 23,000ft (7.01km), (H) 26,500ft (8.06km) at 155,000lb (70,310kg); range (H, max payload) 2,487 miles (4,002km); ferry range (H, with reserves) 4,606 miles (7,412km); take-off to 50ft (15m) (H) 5,160ft (1,573m) at 175,000lb (79,380kg); landing from 50ft (15m) (H) 2,700ft (823m) at 100,000lb (45,360kg).

**Armament:** None.

**History:** First flight (YC-130A) 23 August 1954, (production C-130A) 7 April 1955; service delivery December 1956.

**Users:** USA.

**Below: One of the most visibly different versions of the C-130 is the EC-130E battlefield command and control platform, whose 20 communications systems require extra aerials (antennae) ahead of the fin and in pods under the outer wings. This example is operated by the 7th Airborne Command and Control Squadron at Keesler.**

The versatility of the C-130 Hercules has made the aircraft a natural choice for many specialised applications, several of them for electronics use. The EC-130E is a modified C-130E produced by the Lockheed Aircraft Service Company (LASC) to replace the EC-121 (Super Constellation) in USAF service. The EC-130E has a 40ft (12.2m) Airborne Battlefield Command and Control Centre (ABCCC) capsule in the hold, fitted with special communications equipment and accommodation for 12–16 people. There are some very unusual blade antennae beneath each wing and forward of the fin, and three trailing-wire antennae can be deployed from streamlined canisters beneath each wing and under the rear fuselage. These aircraft serve with the 7th Airborne Command and Control Squadron of 552 AWAC Wing at Keesler Air Force Base, Mississippi.

►

**Above: An almost head-on view of an EC-130E, showing the extreme narrowness of the giant blade aerials under the outer wings, just inboard of the cigar-shaped pods. The latter, plus a third installation in the rear fuselage, can deploy three trailing wires each several kilometres in length for use at very low frequencies.**

Above: This MC-130E clandestine multirole variant serves with the chief USA user, the 7th Special Operations Squadron of the 1st Special Operations Wing at Hurlburt Field, Florida.

Right: Another MC-130, pictured at a typical nap-of-the-Earth height at which these well-equipped machines fly most of their missions. Note the nose pick-up recovery system and special systems at the extreme tail. EW installations help protect the MC.

▶ The MC-130E is a little-known version serving with the 1st Special Operations Squadron, 3rd Tactical Fighter Wing. It has special avionics equipment, including an ALQ-8 ECM pod under the port wing, and two of its uses are for clandestine exfiltration and airdrop missions. No aircraft in the world try harder to survive at low levels.

Four EC-130Gs were built for the US Navy for the TACAMO (Take Charge and Move Out) role, later supplemented by 16 EC-130Qs with improved equipment and crew accommodation. This system is intended to provide survivable communications to submerged ballistic missile submarines (SSBN). One aircraft is always airborne over the Atlantic and a second over the Pacific; the primary downlink to the SSBNs is by Very Low Frequency (VLF) using a 6.2 mile (10km) trailing-wire antenna and a 100kW transmitter, and when it is necessary to transmit the aircraft banks in a continuous circle, which leaves the greater part of the antenna hanging vertically below.

Left: Ground close-up of the underwing installations of an EC-130E. In this case the outboard VLF trailing-wire pods are painted grey, matching the giant "axe-blade" aerials further inboard. Just visible at extreme left is the large blade aerial on the right side of the rear fuselage. Further forward, under the wing, is an extremely large pod which serves a heat exchanger. This aircraft is USAF No 63-9817.

The EC-130H is an electronic warfare aircraft in the Compass Cell programme and entered service with the USAF in 1982. No further details have been published.

A recent proposal by the Lockheed Aircraft Service Company is for a version known as the EC-130 Airborne Radar Extension (ARE). The ARE would have the APS-125 radar of the E-2C Hawkeye, with the circular radome mounted on top of a shortened fin. This would give all the facilities of the very successful E-2C, but with much greater operating space and endurance. It would also have attractions for air forces which require an AEW/AWACS capability and which already operate the C-130 in the transport role.

Another recent proposal was a Lockheed submission for a replacement for the EC-130G and Q in the TACAMO mission. This would have been powered by three GE/SNECMA CFM56 turbofans, but it lost out to the Boeing E-6A (*qv*).

# Tupolev Tu-126

## Tu-126 Moss

**Origin:** The OKB named for Andrei N. Tupolev.
**Type:** Airborne Warning and Control System (AWACS) platform.
**Powerplant:** Four 15,000ehp Kuznetsov NK-12MV turboprops.
**Dimensions:** Span 168ft (51.2m); overall length 181ft 1in (55.2m); height 52ft 8in (16.05m); wing area 3,350 sq ft (311m²).
**Weights:** Maximum take-off 375,000lb (170,000kg).
**Performance:** Maximum speed 530mph (850km/h); range 7,785 miles (12,550km); normal operational endurance 18hr.
**Armament:** None.
**History:** First flight 1962-64; service delivery about 1967.
**Users:** Soviet Union.

Initially seen in a cine film released in 1967, this aircraft was the first airborne surveillance and control platform to be developed in the USSR. It was a conversion of the Tu-114 civil airliner but used almost the same wing, propulsion units and undercarriage as the "Bear" family of military aircraft. The Tu-126 is, in fact, slightly larger than the Bear, with a dramatically larger fuselage and extended-chord wing flaps, and with outstanding qualities of range, endurance and accommodation. A crew of 12 is carried.

The rotating radome is, at 36ft 1in (11m) diameter, some 6ft (1.83m) larger than that of the Boeing E-3A (*qv*) and has been given the NATO reporting name "Flat Jack". Other features include a flight refuelling probe, 21 visible avionic blisters or flush aerials, a large ventral fin used for various services, and an extended tail cone carrying further electronics. Called

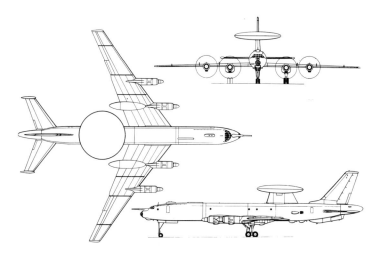

**Above: Three-view of Tu-126 in mid-1970s configuration. Various small features appeared subsequently on the fuselage and tailcone.**

**Below: The Tu-126 has a very deep rotodome aerial, with the main dielectric "windows" appearing black.**

"Moss" by NATO, these aircraft have been in service for some 15 years and certainly represent an earlier state of the art than USAF and RAF surveillance platforms, although the official US assessment, "ineffective over land and only marginally effective over water", could be misleading. In many exercises, and in the Indo-Pakistan war of 1971, the Tu-126 has gained enough experience not only to underpin the next generation (SUAWACS) but also to fly vital patrols in particularly sensitive areas where interceptors and other aircraft, not only of the PVO, need airborne control. Only about 15 airframes were constructed, of which about 10 are currently operational with Voyska PVO; if they have no life problems they could be progressively updated and remain in service for many years.

The Tu-126 is apparently intended to operate in conjunction with interceptor aircraft to detect and destroy incoming low-flying strike aircraft. A fleet of ten, of which only some 75 percent would be serviceable, is quite insufficient to provide coverage of more than a very limited area of the USSR. The successor to the Tu-126—the Il-76 SUAWACS—is now undergoing flight trials.

**Left: Though better than sweeping US assessments, the Tu-126 is an interim aircraft. Propeller/radar interference must be heavy.**

# Westland Sea King

## Sea King AEW Mk 2

**Origin:** Westland Helicopters, Yeovil, UK (licence from Sikorsky).
**Type:** Airborne early warning helicopter.
**Powerplant:** Two Rolls-Royce Gnome (derived from GE T58) free-turbine turboshafts; past production mostly 1,500shp Gnome H.1400, current 1,590shp H.1400-1, future 1,795shp H.1400-3.
**Dimensions:** Diameter of five-blade main rotor 62ft (18.9m); overall length (rotors turning) 72ft 8in (22.15m); fuselage length 55ft 10in (17.02m); height (rotors turning) 16ft 10in (5.13m).
**Weights:** Empty 16,873lb (7,654kg); maximum loaded (H.1400-1 engines) 21,000lb (9,525kg).
**Performance:** Maximum speed 143mph (230km/h); typical cruising speed 131mph (211km/h); maximum (not vertical) rate of climb 1,770ft (540m)/min; approved ceiling 10,000ft (3.05km); range (maximum load) about 350 miles (563km), (maximum fuel) 937 miles (1,507km).
**Armament:** None.
**History:** Derived from Sikorsky S-61 of 1959; first flight (Sea King) 7 May 1969, (AEW) July 1982.
**Users:** UK (RN).

In the South Atlantic conflict in 1982 the Royal Navy quickly discovered that whilst Sea Harriers and helicopters went some way towards replacing the carrier-borne fixed-wing tactical air force of the old fleet carriers there

was one glaring deficiency: airborne early warning. As a result, some Argentine attacks were not detected until too late and the British ships suffered some grievous losses. The reason for this is simple: the attacking aircraft were approaching at some 600mph (965km/h), or 10 miles (16.1km) per minute; at such speeds the rotation rate of a ship's radar (typically 6 revolutions per minute) becomes a major factor, and in the 30-40 seconds necessary to verify the target the latter will be 6.6 miles (10.62km) closer.

The only feasible way to cope with this problem was a "quick-fix", in which a modified Thorn-EMI Searchwater radar of the type used in the Nimrod MR Mk 2 was installed in a Westland Sea King HAS Mk 2 helicopter. This undertaking, which might have occupied two years in peacetime conditions, was achieved in less than two months. The radar scanner is mounted on a pylon on the starboard side of the aircraft inside an inflatable protective dome, which swivels backwards through 90° when not in use. With modified antenna and computer software, this radar enables the helicopter to detect aircraft at considerable range—approximately 115 miles (185km)—as well as monitoring surface targets. This is an effective if somewhat expensive solution, but it is the only answer for navies without large fleet carriers.

**Below: Westland had proposed this valuable radar picket Sea King version long before 1982 but no funds were made available. The result was a crash programme to meet an urgent need. Many countries are now interested in this unique VTOL platform.**

# Reconnaissance Systems

The first reconnaissance system was the handwritten note-pad, followed by the hand-held camera. In late 1914 the Royal Flying Corps produced the first specially designed air reconnaissance camera with a fixed-distance lens focused on a glass photographic plate. Modern PR (photo-recon) personnel will be amazed to learn that to take the first photograph the observer, leaning out into the biting wind, had to carry out 11 separate operations with his frozen fingers. Each subsequent exposure was easier, only ten operations being called for.

Since then, cameras have got better. Most are about as big as a suitcase but some are much smaller, especially those carried by RPVs, while for work at extreme altitudes, or from space satellites, some cameras are enormous (and fantastically costly) in order that newspaper headlines shall be readable from a range of perhaps 100 miles (161km). Cameras can point in any desired direction — vertical, forward, oblique or under manual command on gimballed mounts — and modern installations often include a panoramic camera equipped with a rotating prism or rotating lens to give 180° horizon-to-horizon coverage. Compared with the World War II fan of one vertical and two obliques, this saves much time in handling the film and trying to match up three sets of prints, because each picture is a horizon-to-horizon strip.

The panoramic camera is especially accurately adjusted to match the V/h (velocity to aircraft height) ratio. Obviously, a Tornado flying at 800kt (1,500km/h), at 200ft (90m) is going to need a different setting from an aircraft flying more slowly at a much greater height above the ground. Modern TRFs (terrain-following radars) assist in avoiding blurred images by maintaining a fairly uniform distance from the aircraft to the ground, even in hilly country.

Framing cameras take a succession of individual pictures, each overlapping the next by a small or large amount which the pilot can select. Invariably the lens aperture is adjusted automatically to the ambient light intensity, film type and other variables. Some installations are set to take a single picture, or fast sequence, as soon as the night is illuminated by one or more photoflash cartridges ejected by the aircraft. These in turn are timed to go off at the moment the camera is pointing at the target, which may be attacked on the same high-speed run by the aircraft itself. Mission strike cameras usually take single pictures, timed to show the results of the attack, or a panoramic strip along the aircraft track. In contrast, recon strips are invariably cross-track, so that when all the strips are laid parallel they give a giant picture of a very large area, which at high altitude can extend 100 miles (161km) or more on each side. Obviously, towards the edges the coverage is poor, partly because of distance and partly because of the almost horizontal "grazing angle", which is usually much less informative than near-vertical coverage.

Not only have cameras changed greatly, but film has been improved out of all recognition. One of the obvious things the military commander needs is a better picture. In 1917 the observer holding a camera at 15,000ft (4.5km) was unable to bring back a picture showing anything other than gross features such as trenches, well-used paths or tracks, buildings and

**Right: A famous 1939 photograph taken by a Luftwaffe He 111 showing near misses on British warships at Rosyth, Firth of Forth. The Forth Bridge can be seen top right.**

possibly large vehicles. Camouflage could be extremely effective. Thus, the film producer had to do two things: increase the fine-grain structure of the film, to show finer detail, and find a way to defeat camouflage. Today the camera has been augmented by a host of other devices that use optical wavelengths (visible light), microwaves (TV or Vidicon cameras), radar wavelengths (such as the SLAR or SAR) or heat waves (IR or linescan). Each has its own advantages and disadvantages.

Optical cameras can be loaded with film of such sensitivity and small grain size that it is possible to read a car licence or a soldier's badges of rank from a height of 100 miles (161km), the nominal altitude of the lowest practical orbiting satellite. As for camouflage, as early as the Korean War colour film was printing living vegetation green and other subjects in shades of pink or other contrasting colours. Thus bushes or branches piled on a tank would quickly die and show up not as green but as tell-tale pink. By the early 1950s so-called false-colour film, exposed through a pale yellow filter, virtually defeated any simple camouflage. From Ektachrome Infrared Aero 8443 film has now been derived even more advanced films which are sensitive both to visible light and to other wavelengths, not only including infra-red. Making things invisible to the human eye is no longer good enough, and such things as large foliage-covered nets are little more than morale-boosters unless they are extremely sophisticated and costly. ▶

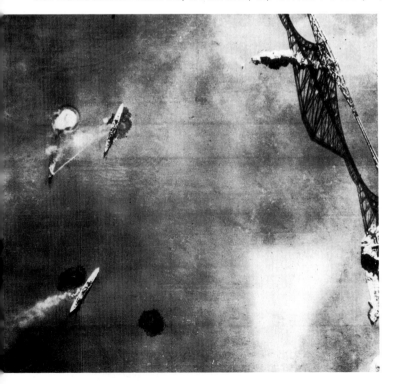

►    Today there are many other factors affecting aerial reconnaissance, but first it is necessary to look at modern sensors other than optical cameras. The first to be developed historically was radar, which as early as 1939 was being used in Britain to generate a PPI (Plan Position Indication) using a beam orbiting around a vertical axis below the aircraft. The first production mapping radars were used to fix aircraft position or find surface or ship targets, but by the Korean War reconnaissance radars were enabling radar-type photographs to be obtained giving a "hard copy" print that could be brought back for analysis. The next stage was to alter the wavelength and aerial array in order to produce a more useful beam swept out to one side of the aircraft track. This SLAR (Side-Looking Aircraft Radar) comprises a power source generating intense microwave signals which are fed along a waveguide which, if it is desired to map to both left and right, is split to channel half the energy to each of two aerials. The latter comprises multi-element phased emitters which send out a very narrow sheet-like beam to left or right and inclined down to strike the surface.

   Thus the SLAR sweeps across the ground below and out to either or both sides of the aircraft's track, the return signals being used to generate a picture of the ground which can either be stored on film or turned into a video (TV) signal and transmitted or even, in a modern set, converted into a stream of digital pulses. SLARs must have an aerial array that is stabilised in pitch, yaw and roll, so that it is possible to point the array independently of the motion of the aircraft. Obviously there are limits to the angular motion, and violent aircraft manoeuvres would prevent proper pictures from being received. In order to get MTI (Moving-Target Indication) and imagery from fixed targets it is essential to maintain correct doppler differences in frequency between the signals sent back by the ground, or a house, and, say, a moving armoured car. Thus, as it is impossible for the pilot to maintain an absolutely exact course or airspeed, or avoid flying through gusts of wind (especially at low level), special electronic circuits are included to cancel out all changes in aircraft speed and direction and thus allow the SLAR to spot targets on the ground that really are moving.

   The APD-10 radar carried by reconnaissance RF-4 Phantoms has the added feature of a stabilised horn transmitter, faired under a small blister

**Below: A typical example of today's counterpart of traditional air photography, using optical cameras, is this strip of three sequenced frames taken by a Luftwaffe RF-4E Phantom flying at Mach 0.8 (speed given as 955km/h) at 500ft (150m). The camera, on Station 1, was a Zeiss KRb 8/24, with auto exposure control and a yellow filter matched with Kodak Plus-X 2402 film. In the lower strip the optical distortion has been automatically corrected.**

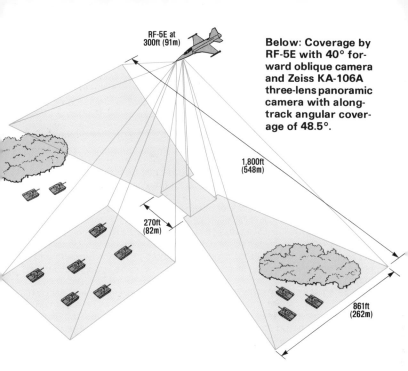

RF-5E at
300ft (91m)

**Below: Coverage by
RF-5E with 40° for-
ward oblique camera
and Zeiss KA-106A
three-lens panoramic
camera with along-
track angular cover-
age of 48.5°.**

1,800ft
(548m)

270ft
(82m)

861ft
(262m)

on the aircraft, which can transmit the video picture direct to a friendly
aircraft or any other station within LOS (line of sight) range. Normally,
however, the received radar signals are displayed on two CRTs (cathode-
ray tubes) which are continuously photographed on film 9½in (241mm)
wide. The scale on the film is 1:1,000,000, and unlike an ordinary camera
(the scale of which is obviously distorted all the way from vertically ▶

**Below: Most versions of the Grumman OV-1 Mohawk are equipped
with optical cameras, and the OV-1D has three. Shown here is the
KS-61 panoramic camera which gives horizon-to-horizon coverage.
There is also a standard vertical camera and a forward-looking
panoramic camera, and usually an IR sensor and a SLAR (side-
looking airborne radar) in an external pod. US Army Mohawks are
now being updated.**

▶ beneath the aircraft to the horizon) scale is constant at all distances or directions. The distance along track between successive strips is governed by aircraft speed, so that it is possible accurately to measure the distance between, say, two trees. Lateral ranges can be slant ranges or they can easily be converted to distances measured along the ground; in a low-level run there is little difference. As in all other SLARs the film is interrupted about every 5 miles (8km) for automatic insertion of a brief data block giving such items as aircraft identity, mission, geographical location (inputted by an INS or other source) and date/time.

Largely by combining high-speed computers with the radar it has been possible today to generate vastly improved pictures. Without going into too much technical detail, DBS (Doppler Beam-Sharpening) and the SAR (Synthetic-Aperture Radar) both use software to process the signals in such a way that the image is made very much sharper and capable of showing much greater detail. Even fighter radars, such as the F-15's APG-63, can be upgraded by SAR techniques to give roughly ten times better picture resolution. The SAR phases the emitted and received signals in such a way that they appear to come not in a series from a single small aerial moving through the sky but in single giant pulses from an enormous aerial half a mile or more in length, arranged along the track of the aircraft. An aerial of such dimensions could give marvellous picture definition, the only snag being that different bits of each built-up picture are not seen at exactly the same time.

Much more can be done with what can best be described as radars, because they operate at microwave wavelengths in the region of millimetres to centimetres, but we must now turn to another part of the electromagnetic spectrum where the wavelengths are much shorter. Right next to visible light is the region we call infra-red (IR), the radiation of which we also call heat. The longest IR waves are taken to have a wavelength of 1,000 micrometres (1mm), and they go on to join visible red light at 0.7 micrometre. We can use them to tell us about targets in the same way we use the much longer waves of radar. There is one great advantage: everything around us is extremely hot compared with absolute zero ($-273^{\circ}$C), so it emits IR radiation; thus the IR reconnaissance system does not need to betray its presence by sending out any emissions, but can be a purely passive system doing nothing but sensing the incoming signals, just like our own eyes. There is also a small drawback: the small waves are rapidly attenuated by moisture, water vapour and dust in the atmosphere, which causes severe absoption and scattering, and at some wavelengths the atmospheric transmission is virtually zero. But in good weather there is no problem in

the band from 8 to 12 micrometres, and in the region of 10.6 micrometres many hundreds of IR sensors have been developed in many countries.

To reduce cost it has been found possible to use standard parts in large numbers of IR sensors in each country, resulting in what are called Common Module systems which can be built into complete installations for reconnaissance aircraft, fighters, helicopters, tanks and warships. Fighter and attack aircraft use what are called FLIRs (Forward-Looking IR), but the reconnaissance aircraft uses a downwards-looking surveillance sensor called IRLS (IR Linescan). All IR sensors are based on some kind of detector which, when made very cold to minimise "noise" due to its own temperature, is very sensitive to IR radiation. The incoming radiation has to be focused just like the light entering a camera, and the "optical system" usually not only does the focusing but also, by means of spinning mirrors or prisms, feeds the detector with IR from a 360° ring in the vertical plane, rotating about an axis parallel with the fuselage. Thus, as the aircraft is moving forward, the detector sees a succession of strips of the ground, each covering a fresh area.

Obviously we do not want to have any gaps between one strip and the next, but we do not want too much overlap either. The IRLS is therefore adjusted to give just the right strip-to-strip overlap, and the V/h ratio is adjusted automatically to keep the overlap correct no matter whether the aircraft is flying at 350 or 600kt or at 200 or 2,000ft. But how does it work? The sensitive detector is invariably of the photoconductive type. It is a tiny piece of semiconductor material, such as CMT (cadmium mercury telluride) or lead sulphide, which becomes far more conductive as soon as heat radiation is focused on it. A few IRLSs use indium antimonide (InSb) sensitive to 3-5 micrometre radiation. The lenses and prisms used, incidentally, are not glass because glass is an effective barrier to heat, but of special glassy material with high transparency to IR wavelengths. As soon as the system is switched on, the refrigeration comes into action, either using violently expanded air (the so-called Joule-Thomson effect) as in the British Aerospace 401 used in the Jaguar recon pod, or else by circulating liquid nitrogen at −196°C. The optics then start feeding in strips of terrain, and the FOV (field of view) can be adjusted to anything the user thinks most advantageous. The distant view near the horizon may not be very useful, and 150° (75° to left and right) is a fair compromise, though the Type 401 just mentioned is set at 120° because Jaguars fly very low. Obviously the optics must be roll-stabilised to the greatest practical bank-angle so that the aircraft can weave and manoeuvre without spoiling the accuracy of the picture. ▶

**Left: Typical of the largest sizes of IRLS is the BAe Dynamics Type 401 described in the text above. It is a substantial unit with a length of 23¾in (604mm) and weight of 74.8lb (34kg).**

**Right: All photographers are familiar with yellow filters, and various large examples are in common use on aerial reconnaissance cameras. Here one is inspected by S/Sgt Muriel Giorgi.**

**Left: Typical of light Co-In type camera pods is this Vinten installation on a Pilatus Britten-Norman Defender.**

**Right: Close-up of the BAe Dynamics multi-sensor pod carried by the Jaguars of RAF No 41 Sqn at Coltishall on recon missions.**

▶ The detector responds virtually instantaneously to the changing temperatures coming to it from grass, lakes, concrete, tiled roofs, power station chimneys and blast furnaces. Input from a cool lake causes a small electric current to flow from the detector, but a blast furnace would cause a suddenly much greater current. The varying electric current forms a video (TV type) signal, which can be displayed line by line on a screen just like a black-and-white TV; alternatively, it can be recorded on magnetic tape or film, or sent to a ground station or processed or stored in other ways. If we simply feed a TV screen we see a picture rather like a photographic negative, but with the important difference that we are recording not light but heat. This can provide even more information than an optical camera. We can see the white areas of a twin-jet that has had its engines running for more than a few seconds. We can see the jet-black inner wings of another that has just landed, its fuel still frozen from being at 40,000ft (18km) altitude. A clear dark-grey aircraft outline on the sun-baked concrete shows where an aircraft has just taxied away, this area having previously been in shadow. A white streak on the same concrete shows the hot area impinged upon by a jet engine.

We must not forget that today the reconnaissance platform has to bring back as much information as possible on the enemy's emitters. His radio stations, radars, electronic data-links and even mobile stations such as tanks or aircraft must all be investigated. This is called Elint (electronic intelligence) for the radars and related devices and Comint (communications intelligence) for simple radio messages. The task in each case calls for finding the enemy's operating frequencies, recording the transmissions, and in almost all cases also plotting the location of the source by TOA (time of arrival), DOA (direction of arrival) or triangulation techniques if we are

using several listening stations. As the enemy will clearly use advanced techniques to try to defeat us, such as "spread spectrum" and frequency hopping in which the frequency never stays the same from one millionth of a second to the next, we have to be clever if we are to get comprehensive or even usable recordings.

Any reconnaissance sensor can be installed inside a dedicated reconnaissance aircraft, i.e. one that is used for no other purpose. A few reconnaissance aircraft, such as the RF/A-18A Hornet, may also carry weapons, but this is very unusual. The true reconnaissance aircraft, such as some of the large maritime Soviet Tupolevs or the USAF's TR-1 or SR-71, are incapable of flying any other kind of mission, and contain installations that could never be fitted into a practical combat aircraft. But sensors can also, if they are small enough, be packaged inside an RPV, the subject of a separate section of this book, or inside a streamlined pod which can be hung on one of the pylons of a fighter or attack aircraft.

Thus, while the US and Soviet air forces use dedicated recon aircraft such as the RF-4C, TR-1, Tu-16 Badger and MiG-25R, the Royal Air Force has no overland recon aircraft except a squadron of Jaguars, and another of Harriers, both of which can clip on small pods. Both the Buccaneer and Tornado could make good dedicated recon platforms, and in fact MBB in West Germany has developed a pod for the latter aircraft. Whether a podded combat aircraft is a good bargain is a matter of swings and roundabouts; obviously the dedicated aircraft has greater capability, both in sensors and in communications, and possibly also in dispensed countermeasures or photoflash cartridges, but it costs more to buy and operate.

There remains one final vital factor. Reconnaissance information is probably the world's most perishable commodity. Everything possible must ▶

**Left: Swedish FFV Red Baron pod under a Danish RF-35 Draken, opened to show the IRLS. Pod weight is 276lb (125kg).**

**Right: The US Navy has retired its dedicated recon aircraft and at present uses F-14 Tomcats with this Tarps pod.**

▶ be done to get it to the person in need of it in the shortest possible time. As early as 1916 recon aircraft were dropping carefully packaged stacks of glass-plate photographs plus handwritten notes over the local army HQ prior to landing back at their own airfield, and we are all familiar with ground crews feverishly getting at large camera magazines and sprinting to a waiting bike or car. The RF-4C introduced the capability of inflight processing of the film, quite apart from its radio data-link. In its day the world's most advanced recon platform was the US Navy's RA-5C Vigilante, which could fly at Mach 2 at 60,000ft (18km) whilst gathering information into a battery of cameras, a large SLAR and a major Elint installation. (There is a story of a photo interpreter who measured a US football field in the SLAR printout during early RA-5C tests and found the field 5ft too short; they measured the field and guess what—it was 5ft too short.) The big advance with the RA-5C was that it introduced a secure data-link back to the carrier or command surface warship which, as part of the IOIS (Integrated Operational Intelligence System), went far towards cutting out the time delay between gathering the information and getting it in usable form to the recipient.

No matter whether aeroplanes, helicopters, RPVs or satellites are used, the objective today is RTR (real-time recon). Information now is perhaps ten times as valuable as the same information in 30 minutes, and to have it in an hour may be of no value at all. By using satellites as relay stations, recon platforms can never be out of LOS range of the base station, and it is often not too difficult to process the incoming information into a form suitable for sending back by a radio data-link. The problems are still large. One is that unambiguous transmission is needed, undegraded by enemy ECM; this means a digital data-link, called a downlink because it beams the information from air to ground, with particular anti-jam properties. Another, for which we do not have the space to consider here, is a factor affecting all combat aircraft: the platform must be survivable, in other words it must fly the mission without being shot down. Perhaps the most intractable problem of all is that for the best resolution we must work not with radar or IR but at optical wavelengths.

In the past this has inevitably involved hurrying spools of film through some kind of wet developing process, with rapid drying and the production of prints. This is compounded in difficulty if the film is of an advanced colour or false-colour type, and it is vital not only to get prints of the highest quality but also not to stretch or distort the film or prints because distances have to be measured. Not the least of the problems at optical wavelengths— certainly with ordinary cameras, which "see" as we do—is that, as noted earlier, the horizon-to-horizon distance scale varies enormously. An inch of print looking vertically downwards may be a distance on the ground of 100ft (33m), whereas the final inch to the horizon may contain a ground distance of many miles.

Obviously the Soviet Union is well advanced with new systems that will meet all requirements, and so are many other countries, but the only one to keep the world constantly informed of its progress is the USA. Both USAF AFAL (Air Force Avionics Lab) and the Navy Electronic Systems Command, and certain other agencies, have been working for almost ten years on devices able to work at optical wavelengths but also send the information to the ultimate recipient in real time. The chief system is the USAF ESSWACS (Electronic Solid-State Wide-Angle Camera System), first flown at Eglin AFB in an RF-4C in August 1978 but vastly refined since then. It takes in the scene through five independent lens assemblies which focus the light on to five CCDs. A CCD (charge-coupled device) is almost the optical analogue of the IR detector in that it is a solid-state detector which emits a current when irradiated. Each CCD has an FOV of 140° and the long axis of each CCD is transverse, i.e. at 90° to the aircraft track.

The five electric currents are fed through a video processor and multiplex system to break them down into a single stream of jam-proof digital pulses. These will normally be recorded in the aircraft on magnetic

**Above: Real-time synthetic-aperture radar picture (above) taken with the F-15's Hughes APG-63 radar, together with (top) optical camera photograph. Note the One-Eleven parked on the runway.**

tape, but the vital "extra" is that they are simultaneously transmitted by data-link (possibly via satellite) to the ultimate recipient. Here the digital signal is rebuilt into pictures, each in the form of closely spaced parallel lines, as in TV. Each line is made up of 8,640 pixels (picture elements), which at 1,000ft (328m) represents a ground distance of about 5,400ft (1,650m); this can be equally divided left/right, or offset to either side of the aircraft. Unlike normal photography, the distance scale is constant, and thus lengths can be measured anywhere on each line in the knowledge that they will be accurate. The rate at which the CCDs are read depends on aircraft ground speed, giving accurate line spacing at all times.

ESSWACS and its rivals are the prototypes for tomorrow's aerial spy systems, working also at IR wavelengths for improved night and anti-camouflage capability. Together with vastly improved Elint, they will lay bare everything the "bad guys" are even thinking about.

# Remotely Piloted Vehicles

## ARGENTINA
### FMA
The FMA (Fábrica Militar de Aviones) at Córdoba has resurrected studies on multirole reconnaissance/attack RPVs derived from the FMA IA 59 target RPV. Any vehicle capable of making the round trip from the mainland to the Falklands would have to be a fresh design.

## AUSTRALIA
### GAF Jindvik
Having been in production over 30 years, this is one of the world's most highly developed targets, but it appears that not one of the 540-plus ordered has been for any alternative purpose. The extra high-altitude version with doubly-extended wingspan can fly at 67,000ft (20.4km) and has a range of 1,036 miles (1,668km) and could be a valuable surveillance platform.

## BELGIUM
### MBLE Epervier (Sparrowhawk)
This is a typical example of a NATO programme. Carefully planned throughout the 1960s to meet NATO specifications for a battlefield surveillance system, it received Belgian Government support from July 1969, and in 1974 went into production for the Belgian Army. No other NATO country showed interest, and total production was just 43, plus associated ground equipment. Epervier has a span of 67.75in (1.72m), a length of 93.75in (2.38m) and a launch weight of 313lb (142kg), carrying Omera or Oude-Delft optical cameras of 70 or 127mm focal length and SAT Cyclope IR linescan with real-time transmission. The engine is a Lucas CT3201 (originally called the Rover, later Alvis, TJ125) turbojet of 114lb (52kg) thrust. Missions are flown up to a maximum radius of 47 miles (75km) at 311mph (500km/h) at heights below 6,000ft (1,830m).

## CANADA
### Canadair CL-89 (USD-501)
This RPV is unique in that not only was it adopted by several major NATO countries but it also led to an international programme (CL-289, described later) which is probably the world's leading tactical surveillance RPV. From the start the need was for high survivability over the battlefield, so the concept was that of a high-speed missile rather than a microlight aeroplane. Canadair began work in 1959, with funding by Canada (which handled all the hardware) and the UK; West Germany joined as a one-third partner in 1965. Over 500 USD-501s were produced, and each had made on average more than five flights by late 1983. The system is in service with the three sponsor nations plus France and Italy, half of each Italian system being licence-made by Meteor SpA. There are foreplanes for pitch/yaw and ailerons on the cruciform rear wings for roll control. The 8ft 6½in (2.6m) RPV is fired from a truck launcher by a tandem boost rocket which increases weight from 238lb (108kg) to 343lb (156kg). Missions are flown at up to 10,000ft (3km) at 460mph (741km/h) over radii up to about 36 miles (58km), or 43 miles (69km) with an extra fuel tank. Basic sensors are a Zeiss optical camera, used with 12 automatic photoflares, and a BAe Dynamics IR linescan. Recovery is by a parachute and inflatable airbags.

Left: It is possible that Canadair may succeed where the British Shorts and Dornier of West Germany failed. The CL-227 seen here could be the first small VTOL recon RPV to find customers. It has obvious advantages in combat deployment flexibility, for it can rise from a small truck and after each mission be brought back for a soft landing. The chief drawbacks to this class of RPV are low speed and high fuel consumption, meaning limited range and endurance. Service 227s would not be brightly painted.

## Canadair CL-227

This small, peanut-shaped system is a highly survivable and very easily used device which probably has an enormous future. It can be launched from the ground or from its truck or transport platform. It climbs vertically away with contraprops driven by a 32hp Williams WR34-15-2 turboshaft, and can translate into forward flight at 82mph (132km/h) and operate over radii of up to 31 miles (50km) at heights to 10,000ft (3km). At any point it can stop and hover, presenting a tiny radar or IR target undetected by ear; if necessary it can be tethered (for example, to small ships). The engine is in the upper bulge, and the lower section houses the sensors which can include daylight TV, LLTV, a laser designator, a thermal imager, a radiation detector and decoy equipment. Lift-off weight is 276lb (125kg), yet the 227 can fly for 3hrs and carry out detailed surveillance or target acquisition. There are likely to be many customers.

# CHINA

Though the only vehicle in this class so far disclosed is the simple Changcheng B-2 target, its engine, the 16hp Huosai-16 piston engine, is said to be suitable for other types of RPV which are probably being developed.

# FRANCE

### Aérospatiale R20

Though overshadowed by the more numerous (1,550-plus) CT.20 target version, this swept-wing jet reconnaissance vehicle has been in regular use by the French Army since 1964. Its basic design, by Nord-Aviation, closely ▶

▶ followed the pioneer American Firebee, and the engine was the same as in the first Firebees, a Turboméca Marboré II turbojet of 880lb (400kg) thrust. The R.20 is fired by two solid boost rockets from its Berliet truck and then climbs away at a weight of 1,875lb (850kg), controlled by a butterfly ("V") tail and roll spoilers. Sensors include standard NATO cameras, with night flares and other devices such as an IR scanner in the nose and wingtip pods. At a radius of 62 miles (100km) it can be controlled with a navigational accuracy of 985ft (300m), flying typically at 3,300ft (1km) at Mach 0.65 or some 490mph (790km/h). With three synchronised cameras, the R.20 can photograph over 77 sq miles (200km²) in one sortie. Data, including linescan picture transmission, can be sent back by radio link.

### Marchetti Héliscope
Under contract from the official DRME (directorate of test and research), SA Charles Marchetti has since 1970 been working on tethered surveillance platforms supported by one or three contrarotating rotors driven by electric motors drawing current from the ground. The largest Héliscopes carry 220lb (100kg) of sensors to a height of 755ft (230m).

### Nord 510
From 1966 Nord-Aviation (later absorbed into Aérospatiale) tested the Type 510 tethered flying platform; it had a turboshaft-driven rotor system with control by jet deflection backed up by autostabilisation by three tethers. It operated to 1,000ft (300m). Nord expected to go on with the Type 511, with a single tether and height up to 3,000ft (1km), but work was abandoned in 1969.

# GERMANY (WEST)
### Dornier Kiebitz (Peewit)
Few aviation products have ever been under development for so long without getting into production as this neat tethered helicopter platform. The original design began in the early 1960s and by 1966 was resulting in prototypes powered by a KHD or MAN turboshaft and with a weight of some 551lb (250kg). A notable feature was cold-gas drive, the engine supplying compressed air to tip jets on the rotor blades. In 1972 Dornier received a major MoD contract for an operational system, and the Do 32 Kiebitz grew into the Do 34 with a slightly larger 26ft 3in (8m) rotor powered by a compressor driven by a 420hp 250-C20B. In 1974 an agreement was signed with France which brought in LCT as partner, plus the Orphée II surveillance radar, in a battlefield system called Argus (acronym for "autonomous battlefield reconnaissance system" in German). In September 1981 the French pulled out, but Dornier is continuing development and expects service entry "in the second half of the 1980s". The whole system, with equipment and 24hr fuel, is carried on a 10-ton (10.2-tonne) cross-country truck, from which the RPV can be readied and put into action at its operating height of 985ft (300m) in eight minutes. Attitude and exact position are held steady at all times, and payload packages totalling 309lb (140kg) can include equipment for multisensor reconnaissance, target acquisition, fire control, communications relay or traffic monitoring.

### Dornier LA-RPV
This programme began as the UKF ("pilotless combat aircraft" in German) in 1973. At first an Aeritalia G91R was used as the main test platform, but though this flew with an AEG-Telefunken TV, Eltro FLIR, two-axis stabilisation and a transmitter link, it faded from the scene as the project changed into LA ("air attack") RPV, used for interdiction against strongly defended targets, tactical reconnaissance, defence suppression and EW of various kinds. Several configurations were examined, the favoured one being a miniature aeroplane with an internal weapon bay and an external

dorsal pod for the turbojet (probably a Microturbo TRI 80). Take-off would be rocket-boosted and the landing arrested, and the typical mission would be preprogrammed against a fixed or slowly moving target (no emissions or sensors, and thus immune to all countermeasures), with attack by scatterweapons. Span was 12ft 5½in (3.8m) and length 21ft 4in (6.5m) Development was suspended in 1981 because the Federal DoD was unconvinced of the value of such a delivery system.

### Dornier Hornisse (Hornet)
For over a decade Dornier has studied small RPVs, the completed programmes including the important Locust system (see entry in USA under US DoD) and the KDAR ("anti-radiation mini-RPV" in German) in which the partner was Texas Instruments; the Hornisse mini-RPV is being continued as a company project. It is a tailless delta with a span of 6ft 10½in (2.1m), a length of 6ft 6⅜in (2m), a launch weight of 154lb (70kg) and a speed of 155mph (250km/h) on a 22hp Limbach pusher piston engine. Missions lasting 3hrs at heights up to 10,000ft (3km) can be flown on EO recon, target acquisition and fire control, anti-radar, anti-armour, point-target strike, and target presentation for SAMs or AAA. Sensors can include stabilised TV, autotrack with laser illuminator and passive or active IR or radar seekers used in self-destruct dives on to hostile emitters. Dornier has its own family of microprocessors suitable for Hornisse, but in 1983 was looking for a partner with IR and millimetre-wave radar technology.

**Above: Three Dornier Hornisse mini-RPVs awaiting launch.**

### Dornier MTC II
The Mini-Telecopter II has been on test since March 1981. Two counter-rotating rotors of 10ft 6in (3.2m) diameter are driven by a 40hp Hirth piston engine and lift the 419lb (190kg) vehicle at modest speeds and heights on a 200ft (60m) tether, with radio control in prospect, on missions lasting up to 2hrs. The 132lb (60kg) payload can include stabilised TV or FLIR with autotrack, laser designator, thermal imager, ECM jammer and decoy transmitters. Missions would include battlefield recon, target acquisition and fire control, mine detection, mapping of NBC-contaminated areas, com-link jamming and decoy of anti-ship missiles.

### Dornier Spähplatform

This device ("spotting platform" in German) is an absolute minimum tethered surveillance platform. Carried by a small trailer towed by a Unimog 1.4-tonne truck, it has a 3ft 11¼in (1.2m) rotor with a peripheral ring so that, after being run up to speed by a 33.5hp power source, the rotor takes over a minute to run down. Below the rotor are jet-deflector controls, whilst above it is an optical or TV camera. The platform is launched with the rotor at 4,000rpm, and at a weight of 77lb (35kg) climbs in 10 seconds to the operating height of 164ft (50m). After about 1 minute on surveillance it is quickly reeled back.

### MBB RT 910 Tucan

MBB, biggest aerospace company in West Germany, participated in the KDAR/Locust mentioned under Dornier. The Tucan (Toucan) was taken over with the former VFW company, and unlike most MBB RPV work is based at a division in Bremen called (in English) Naval and Special Technologies. Like Dornier's slightly smaller Mini-RPV, it is a tailless delta, driven by a pusher piston engine. Launch weight is 220lb (100kg) and missions are flown over a radius of 43 miles (70km) including a 30min hold at low level. The sensor is a stabilised TV camera in the nose, with video and other signals sent back by a telemetry link. The wings are adjustable fore and aft to balance the varying payload weight. See International section, Matra/MBB.

**Above: MBB claim that the Tucan is aerodynamically optimised, and another advantage is modular construction, which makes it easy to change payloads under battlefield conditions.**

# INDONESIA
### Lapan XTG-01

In 1975-80 LAPAN, the national aeronautics and space institute in Jakarta, developed a small RPV for photographic and communications-relay purposes. A tractor aeroplane, the XTG-01 was of 7ft 11¾in (2.43m) span, weighed 15.4lb (7kg) and flew at 70mph (112km/h) on a 1.7hp single-cylinder engine, the 0.55gal (2.5l) of fuel giving an endurance of 1hr.

# INTERNATIONAL
### Canadair/Dornier CL-289 (USD-502)

Perhaps the world's most important battlefield surveillance RPV, the CL-289 (NATO designation USD-502) stemmed from the CL-89 described in the Canadian section. Work began in 1975 with Canadair as system manager and ·Dornier as 50/50 subcontractor; France joined in March 1977, SAT having 15 per cent of the work including the IR linescan, with real-time data transmission for ground recording. There is also an optical

**Above: The Canadair/Dornier USD-502 is one of the most important of today's battlefield reconnaissance RPVs. Here one is shown with its finned rocket booster ready to fire.**

sensor, a Carl Zeiss three-lens reconnaissance camera. Span of the rear wings is 4ft 4in (1.32m); length (excluding ADMU probe) is 11ft 10in (3.61m), which is increased to 15ft 4in (4.67m) with the tandem rocket launch booster. The 240lb thrust KHD T117 turbojet gives a speed in the 500mph (800km/h) class, but performance and weight data are classified. Navigation is mainly self-contained, and includes a terrain-following capability based on the doppler to reduce vulnerability (which has been found to be extremely low). Flight trials began in March 1980, contractor trials at Yuma USA Proving Ground were completed in March 1981 and troop trials were completed in August 1982. Production is scheduled to start in 1984.

### Matra/MBB Brevel

In June 1983 Matra of France and MBB of West Germany agreed to develop a new battlefield recon RPV; the name stems from the locations Bremen and Vélizy-Villacoublay. Brevel will be a small propeller-driven vehicle in the 220-331lb (100-150kg) class, with an endurance of several hours carrying a stabilised TV and a FLIR, plus real-time transmission facilities and probably an on-board recorder. The design being worked on combines features of the Matra Scorpion project and MBB Tucan, described previously. It is expected that the operational system will comprise one or more mobile launch trucks and a separate mobile control/receiver station. It could be in service in 1989.

# ISRAEL

### IAI Scout

This highly developed system, used by Israel and export customers, comprises a ground control station, launcher, four to six Scout RPVs and a retrieval net, the operating crew numbering 12. Roles include missile site recon, battlefield control, target identification, strike force control, artillery targeting, border/coastal/waterway surveillance and damage assessment. The configuration is a pusher aeroplane with an 18hp piston engine at the rear of a light-alloy fuselage, the rest being glassfibre. Span is 11ft 9¾in (3.6m), length 12ft 1in (3.68m) and launch weight 260lb (118kg) including mission equipment totalling 50lb (22.7kg). The last includes a stabilised TV camera in a ventral hemispherical dome scanning the entire hemisphere below the RPV. FOV is under remote control from 47.5° to▶

**Above: Rival to the Israeli Scout, the Tadiran Mastiff is shown here in Mk3 form, with an improved tail and increased payload and flight performance. Fixed landing gear can be used for conventional take-offs, but the normal battlefield method is pneumatic launch from an inclined ramp and arrester-wire retrieval.**

▶ 3.4°. A side/side panoramic camera is also fitted, and other sensors can include a laser receiver or designator/ranger and a thermal imager. Speed varies from 63 to 92mph (102-148km/h), and endurance at heights to 10,000ft (3,050m) is 4.5hrs.

### Tadiran Mastiff

A direct competitor to the Scout, the Mastiff has been developed through three major variants, Mk 1 being a small 14hp tractor machine, Mk 2 switching to a twin-boom pusher layout and the current Mk 3 being a bigger model with a 22hp engine, revised tail and more payload and range. Large numbers have been delivered to Israel and export customers, and Tadiran, the biggest electronics/weapon firm in the Middle East, states that the Mastiff has "significant battlefield experience". Missions include real-time recon, remote-control photography, decoy manoeuvres, EW jamming and spoofing, and "other uses within the limitations of payload size and weight". Span is 14ft 1¼in (4.3m), length 9ft 11¾in (3.04m), launch weight 254lb (115kg), payload 66lb (30kg) and endurance 6hrs at 50-80mph (80-130km/h) over radii out to 62 miles (100km) or twice as far with a portable control station.

### Meteor Andromeda (Mirach)

The Andromeda system comprises a series of ground stations, each serving its own function, and a range of different Mirach RPVs. In 1983 the following Mirach models were available: Mirach 20, for target acquisition, designation, surveillance and "kamikaze" attack (22hp engine; weight 154lb, 70kg; speed 112mph, 180km/h; endurance 6hrs); Mirach 70, for surveillance, target acquisition, EW or decoy saturation (70hp engine; weight 573lb, 260kg; speed 193mph, 310km/h; endurance 1hr); Mirach 100, for all tactical missions (253lb Microturbo turbojet; weight 683lb, 310kg; speed 590mph, 950km/h; endurance 1hr 10min); Mirach 300, for multiple roles (750lb Microturbo turbojet; weight 992lb, 450kg; speed Mach 0.9; endurance 2hr 50min); and Mirach 600, for training and evaluation, area recon, defence suppression, attack and EW (two 750lb Microturbo; weight 2,205lb, 1,000kg; speed Mach 0.9; endurance 1hr 50min). Only Mirach 70 was in production (for export) in 1983.

# JAPAN

### Fuji Research RPV

The Japan Defence Agency has appointed Fuji Heavy Industries prime contractor of an RPV for research into unmanned surveillance missions. It will have a span of 11ft 5¾in (3.5m), a length of 7ft 6½in (2.3m) and an empty weight of 198lb (90kg), and will fly at 138mph (222km/h) on a US piston engine after launch by Daicel rocket. Nippon Avionics is handling guidance, Hitachi the TV camera and other companies control and communications.

# SAUDI ARABIA
## MCS PL-60
Mid-Continent Scientific Co of Riyadh stated in 1980 that it had 1,580 of these unusual lightweight machines, which have a high wing, two 1.9hp engines, tailwheel landing gear (conventional take-off and recovery by wire arrester) and a claimed immunity to detection by radar. PL-60A has a span of 10ft 10in (3.3m), a length of 6ft 5in (1.96m), a gross weight of 60lb (27.2kg) and a range of 35 miles (56km) on 0.4gal (1.9l) of fuel. PL-60B has a stiffened structure to carry twice the payload (48lb, 22kg, instead of 25lb, 11.3kg) and has a range of 140 miles (225km) on 1.67gal (7.6l) of fuel. Uses are said to include every kind of surveillance, using an optical or TV camera, as well as "air pollution and weather monitoring".

# SOUTH AFRICA
## National Dynamics Eyrie
Based in Pinetown, Natal, this company's Eyrie is an unconventional device with a Warren-Young (non-stall, non-spin) wing with integral fuselage moulded in glassfibre, Kevlar and carbonfibre, with low-density core, precision moulds making possible rapid and exact production. Radar cross-section is extremely small and the on-board and ground equipment is modular, the system comprising two Eyries (one active, one relay), a gastight mobile ground station, launch and recovery facilities and a maintenance/stowage truck. The RPV has a 30hp engine and ducted pusher propeller, a span of 14ft (4.27m), a length of 11ft 3in (3.43m), a take-off weight of 300lb (136kg) and an endurance of over 5hrs at up to 138mph (222km/h) at heights to 15,000ft (4.57km). Missions include the usual ones plus artillery correction, SAR (search and rescue), EW and ECM and even ground attack with a laser designator and four rockets.

**Above: South African Eyrie, showing its unusual configuration.**

# SOVIET UNION
Though a little is known about Russian target aircraft, nothing at all is known of the country's obviously extensive work in the field of RPVs for many other roles.

# SWEDEN
## FOA Skatan
This short-range, low-cost platform was developed at the FOA (National Defence Research Institute) for daylight recon over the battle area. A miniature aeroplane, it is powered by a 1.6hp engine and weighs only 9.7lb (4.4kg) empty, the take-off weight being up to 16.8lb (7.4kg) depending on the electric-drive camera fitted. Control is by coaxially mounted binoculars of low and high magnification and radio command, with programmed navigation in areas of high ECM. Missions tended to last 10min, over radii to 3 miles (5km) at speeds of up to 62mph (100km/h).

# UNITED KINGDOM

## AEL

Aero Electronics Ltd (AEL), for long a producer of RPVs for many purposes (in recent years chiefly for targets) has so increased its business that in April 1983 it established AEL(RPV) Ltd as a separate company. See MoD Phoenix entry.

### BAe Dynamics Stabileye

British Aerospace Dynamics (Bristol) followed the original FlyBAC, a research programme for RAE Farnborough, with an important series of Stabileyes, beginning with the Mk 1 first flown in October 1974. The Stabileyes are simple vehicles for testing sensors and other equipment items. Over 200 successful flights were made by this initial version in MoD programmes, carrying up to 17.6lb (8kg) of cameras, radar altimeters, missile homing heads and similar payloads. It was followed by Stabileye 2, which had the same twin-boom pusher configuration with a bulbous nacelle and twin fins, but was uprated from 4hp to 7.5hp (Weslake piston engine) and carried almost twice the payload (33lb, 15kg) for twice the time (60 instead of 30mins). The current Mk 3 is redesigned for easy production, with a more box-like nacelle, a single fin and a much greater load-carrying ability of 55lb (25kg). Span is 11ft 11¾in (3.65m), length 9ft 5in (2.87m), launch weight 132lb (60kg) and endurance 2hrs at speeds from 50 to 90mph (81–145km/h). Sensors flown in one programme include IR linescan. In other trials, Stabileye 3s are being assessed as anti-radiation weapons. The engine is a 7hp Weslake, launch is by pneumatic catapult and recovery is either by landing on a skid or by parachute and airbag.

**Above: Stabileye Mk 3 is the latest in the series of mini-RPVs by British Aerospace Dynamics used in numerous MoD and company research programmes. In recent missions IRLS, TV and conventional photographic installations have been evaluated.**

### Intergard GTS 7901 Sky-Eye

Intergard Electronics has achieved several significant sales with unmanned vehicles, including (to two Middle East countries) this close-support information relay mini-RPV. Powered by a pusher piston engine, it has a mixed-construction airframe launched from a four-wheel trolley or by rubber bungee catapult. Guidance is by radio on one of 12 spot frequencies in the 27MHz band (thus 12 can be flown in close proximity on separate channels). Standard payload is a TV camera and real-time transmitter, but alternatives are various multiframe, still or ciné cameras, a laser designator, a chaff dispenser or an ECM active jammer. Span is 8ft (2.44m), length 6ft 8in (2.03m), launch weight 26.5lb (12kg) and endurance up to 30min at 29mph (46km/h); maximum speed is 69mph (111km/h).

## Marconi Machan

Marconi Avionics at Rochester developed the Machan (Hindi word pronounced "m'charn", a treetop platform) with MoD funding as a versatile R&D vehicle with operational possibilities. The Cranfield Institute of Technology is subcontractor for the aluminium/GRP airframe, propulsion system (18hp Weslake with ducted propeller) and digital flight control system. The nose can house various sensors, TV being installed in early tests, and the main objectives are to investigate surveillance, including target recognition and designation, and perfect precision navigation with minimum need for communication to or from the ground. The expected span is 8ft (2.44m), a larger wing with ailerons being also used, and length is 7ft (2.13m); weight on pneumatic catapult launch is 180lb (82kg) and endurance is 2hrs at 74mph (119km/h), maximum speed being twice as fast. Landing is on skids.

## MoD Phoenix

Potentially a major programme, this Ministry of Defence requirement for a battlefield surveillance platform is being worked on by numerous bidders, and replaces the Supervisor project (see Westland). In June 1983 two teams were each awarded a £1 million engineering study contract: Marconi Avionics with Flight Refuelling as main subcontractor, and Ferranti with AEL(RPV) Ltd. The Phoenix system will carry out day/night surveillance and remote battlefield targeting, using advanced avionics and sensors, including one of the UK Thermal Imaging (IR) common modules. A two-way radio datalink will be provided, but naturally it is hoped that autonomous operation will prove practical. Several hundred Phoenix RPVs are needed to back up manned radar-equipped aircraft (described under the Canberra entry) to supply information to British ground forces. They would be used in large numbers with a sophisticated control system not susceptible to countermeasures and allowing individual control of each RPV. For greater security only passive (IR) thermal imagers would be used, the Marconi/FR Phoenix having a Common Module type and the Ferranti/AEL a Rank Pullin imager. Control is likely to be by a frequency-hopping spread-spectrum technique using control in the 10KHz band and digital picture transmission at 1Mbit/sec. An obvious drawback is that thermal imagers are not yet all-weather sensors, but it is expected that manned-air surveillance will find targets to which Phoenix can be sent for a passive look at extremely close range. Service entry is predicted for late 1988.

## RCS

Radio Control Specialists is a producer of numerous families of small, low-cost RPVs for many purposes. Examples include the tailless delta Merlin (4ft 9in, 1.45, span; launch weight 10.5lb, 4.8kg; endurance 30min at 90mph, 145km/h); Falcon (similar but larger, with weight 36lb, 16.3kg, and endurance 45min at 127mph, 204km/h); the tractor 10hp Heron, which can carry small bombs; the very small Swift, with a 2lb (0.9kg) payload; the 9ft 6in (2.9m) span Teledrone II, with two 2hp or one 6hp engine and TV/jammer/chaff options; and the Rotary-Wing RPV, with a 10hp engine, a weight of 44lb (20kg) and an endurance of 1hr at 37mph (60km/h) carrying an 18.7lb (8.5kg) payload which can include stabilised TV or other sensors.

## Short Skyspy

As well as producing various targets, including the Skeet and MATS-B for various customers, Short Brothers devoted large and prolonged effort to the Skyspy VTOL platform for surveillance and many other roles, but never found a customer. The vehicle comprised a propulsion/guidance pod carried above a ducted fan lift system driven by a 65hp engine, with control by thrust vectoring. Much denser than most RPVs, Skyspy was only 3ft 6½in (1.08m) in overall diameter yet could lift off at a weight of 286lb ▶

▶ (130kg) and carry a sensor payload in an external fairing of 44lb (20kg) to 6,000ft (1.83km) on a 90min sortie.

### Vinten/Wallis
In 1981, W. Vinten's Aeronautical Division signed an agreement with Wg Cdr Ken Wallis resulting in trials of Vinten cameras in Wallis autogyros. Trials were then announced of a remotely piloted version able to carry a sensor payload of no less than 353lb (160kg), more than double the limit possible with a manned version.

### Westland Wideye
Westland began working on RPH (remotely piloted helicopter) studies in 1968, leading to flight trials with the small Wisp test vehicle with 5ft (1.52m) coaxial rotors from 1976. This led to the definitive Wideye surveillance RPH with comprehensive sensors, data link and ground systems, as part of the MoD-funded programme called Supervisor. In December 1979 this was cancelled on the grounds of complexity and cost. Westland is continuing to fund Wideye, convinced it is the best solution. Its replacement in MoD thinking is Phoenix (*qv*) and manned aircraft (see Canberra entry in aircraft section).

**Above: The Westland Wideye is no longer funded by the British MoD, but Westland Helicopters is continuing development on a private-venture basis. Features visible here include the small-diameter coaxial rotor and four folding landing legs.**

# UNITED STATES OF AMERICA
### Beech QU-22B
In 1967–70 about three dozen Beech Model 36 Bonanzas were converted into Elint RPV data-relay platforms for use over Vietnam to transmit signals received from Igloo White sensors dropped by friendly aircraft in areas of hostile ground activity. Replacing EC-121 Warning Stars with crews of 26 to 31, the QU-22B still had a man on board but only to monitor the Elint systems.

### Boeing YQM-94A Compass Cope B
Together with the rival Ryan 235, this was probably the biggest and highest-flying RPV ever designed. The USAF Compass Code programme was for an autonomous-sensing Elint collector to take-off and recover from

a runway and fly 30hr missions at 70,000ft (21.34km). Tasks were to include Arctic surveillance of ICBM firings and other activities in the Soviet Union and to replace Pave Nickel B-57s along the Warsaw Pact frontier in Europe. Later it was hoped to use these vehicles as relay stations in the PLSS (Precision-Location/Strike System) to assist USAF attack aircraft. Boeing's contender was started in late 1970 and flew in July 1973. The slender wing had a span of 90ft (27.43m), and weights were 5,500lb (2,494kg) empty and 14,400lb (6,531kg) at take-off with a 700lb (317.5kg) payload for a 24hr mission. Prototypes had a dorsally mounted GE J97 of 5,270lb (2,390kg) thrust, but a turbofan might have been used in production. USAF funding was terminated in July 1977.

### Brunswick decoys
Since 1970 the Brunswick Corporation (previously Celesco) has been testing vehicles carried in multiple by combat aircraft (for example, in F-4 missile recesses) and released to glide on flip-out wings as decoys. Maxi-Decoy flies programmed manoeuvres and carries radar augmenters, jammers and/or other EW payloads at Mach 0.9. The much bigger (7ft 4in, 2.24m, long; 300lb, 136kg) Propelled Decoy has a long-burn motor and flies on autopilot.

### DSI
Developmental Sciences Inc has produced numerous RPVs, Sky Eye being a multimission type with a 12ft 4¾in (3.78m) wing, a pusher propeller and an endurance of 6hrs with 80lb (36kg) of mission equipment which as well as sensors has included rocket tubes and other weapons. Locomp is a Mach 0.82 jet with various payloads.

### E-Systems L450F
First flown (with human pilot) in February 1970, this USAF RPV was a high-altitude, long-endurance (more than 24hrs) reconnaissance vehicle, with a 57ft (17.37m) span and with a 475hp PT6 turboprop in the nose giving a 105mph (170km/h) loiter at 45,000ft (13.7km) with human pilot. The prototype set several world class records.

### E-Systems mini-RPVs
The company has produced 13 families of small vehicles, most being twin-boom pushers with "vertical wings" for direct-force lateral control for extreme agility to avoid enemy fire or improve accuracy in kamikaze attacks. Largest current model is E-200, carrying a payload of user-defined sensors exceeding 100lb (45.4kg) at up to 84mph (136km/h) on 3hr missions over ranges to 161 miles (260km).

### Eglen
This hovercraft company produces and markets the USAF Flight Dynamics Lab Falcon mini-RPV used in large numbers for numerous military/civil purposes.

### Fairchild
Two Fairchild companies were active in the 1970s on many projects, one assisting Sperry convert PQM-102 target aircraft; today, Fairchild Republic is testing the Tactical Mini-Drone for the US Navy, a small 7ft 3in (2.21m) span pusher carrying 50lb (22.7kg) of payload which can include a 30lb (13.6kg) explosive charge when used in the anti-radar harassment role.

### Ford Aerospace
This company's predecessors, Philco-Ford and Aeronutronic Ford, did extensive work on Praeire, Calere and other mini-RPV systems under USAF and Army contracts. Praeire successfully aimed lasers at tank targets for destruction by CLGP and other homing weapons, while Calere usually carried FLIR day/night surveillance systems.

▶

### ▶ Gyrodyne Co of America QH-50D

This remotely piloted helicopter, originally mass-produced for ASW missions from US Navy warships, ended its days as a research RPV carrying a laser ranger/designator, TV, a high-velocity gun and various delivered ordnance.

### Kaman STAPL

The Ship-Tethered Aerial Platform was a 1970-77 remote-control autogyro for maritime surveillance and targeting.

### LMSC Aquila

Biggest of the current US Army efforts, the MQM-105 Aquila grew from a prolonged study by the Lockheed Missiles & Space Co from 1972. LMSC won the US Army's programme for a battlefield surveillance vehicle in 1974, and Aquila vehicles have since passed through many phases although all have been tailless pushers. Current Aquilas have a 26hp engine, a span of 12ft 9in (3.89m), a length of 6ft 10in (2.08m) and a launch weight of 250lb (113kg), and fly over 3hrs within 31 miles (50km) at up to 126mph (203km/h) at up to 12,000ft (3.66km). Launch is by pneumatic catapult and recovery by Dornier ribbon net. Payload has comprised Westinghouse TV and TI FLIR, but target designator, jam-resistant, real-time link and other gear can be provided. A combat unit, delivered in a C-5 Galaxy, comprises five Aquilas, seven trucks, three trailers, 13 troops and the CO. A major achievement is preprogrammed guidance to within 230ft (70m) of a given spot at 12.5 miles (20km) radius.

**Above: Current configuration of the LMSC MQM-105 Aquila.**

### LMSC Aequare

Extensive flying was done with this RPV, which was dropped by a fighter (in a cluster-bomb pod) or fired by a standard SAM and then used for surveillance, target acquisition, laser designation and other tasks, especially in conjunction with friendly attacking manned aircraft. The USAF funding was halted in 1978.

### Martin Marietta 845A (Compass Dwell)

A rebuilt Schweizer SGS 1-34 sailplane, this high-altitude Elint surveillance RPV with a quiet tractor piston engine flew 28hr missions but could not reach 40,000ft (18.14km). It was later, in 1974, given a human pilot and used for upper-air sampling prior to space launches at Cape Canaveral.

### MDAC

McDonnell Douglas Astronautics flew many remotely piloted F-15 models, and was involved in Navy conversion of Phantoms into QF-4Bs, but its own RPV work was limited to a programme flown in 1975-76 under DARPA (Defense Advanced Research Projects Agency) funding with mini-RPVs launched and recovered at sea and in simulated land battle conditions for a wide range of purposes. Typical weight was 150lb (68kg).

**Northrop**
The world's largest builder of RPVs, Northop Ventura's vehicles are nearly all targets but included the NV-128, first flown in May 1974, with a payload of framing and forward oblique cameras or alternatively IR linescan or a panoramic camera. The airframe was a Chukar MQM-74A lengthened to 13ft 4¾in (4.08m), the unchanged Williams WR24-6 turbojet of 121lb (55kg) thrust giving a speed of 518mph (834km/h) at 35,000ft (10.67km).

**Teledyne Ryan**
Teledyne Ryan is by far the most prolific and versatile builder of jet RPVs. The Firebee 1 target made its first guided flights in 1951, well over 30,000 flights by Mk 1s being made subsequently. In 1960, following the loss of Gary Powers, U-2, it proposed a recon version, Red Wagon, which lost funds to the manned SR-71. Work continued and led to:

**Model 147** Originally a modified BQM-34A Firebee with extra fuel and new guidance, Model 147 developed in 1962-64 in the USAF Big Safari programme as an Elint/recon platform which repeatedly penetrated US airspace undetected. Original 147SK Special Recon Aircraft were flown from DC-130s over Communist territory in many areas, wrecks of four being displayed in Peking in May 1965. Later the 100th SRW from Davis-Monthan AFB flew over 2,500 missions over Vietnam, mainly Elint, with mid-air retrieval by CH-53. Important variants were 147H (AQM-34N), a medium-altitude recon used by SAC from 1968; 124I, a hybrid 124/147 widely used by Israel in the Yom Kippur War for recon, Elint and other missions (one decoyed 32 SAMs in one mission and still returned to its base); 147NA (AQM-34G), a medium-altitude ECM platform with active jammer or two underwing chaff dispensers; 147NC (AQM-34H), as AQM34G but heavier and with tailplane end-fins, a payload of Hughes ALQ-71 noise jammers, Westinghouse QRC-335 deception jammers or ALE-2 chaff dispensers; 147NC (AQM-34J), a trainer with Compass Angel Update; 147NC (AQM-34V), the Combat Angel Update of 1974 with a long modular nose housing five E-Systems modular jammers covering three bands plus MB Associates bulk chaff pods; 147SC (AQM-34L and U), low-level photo versions with the later J69 turbojet, more fuel and digital doppler navigation with microwave command, first in Compass Bin/Buffalo Hunter programmes; 147SD (AQM-34M) production variants, some with drop tanks and many fitted to eject Rockwell Elint sensors near hostile emitters to help later manned-aircraft strike; 147RE (AQM-34K), a low-altitude night recon version; 147T (AQM-34P), for high-altitude surveillance (one was displayed in Peking) with span increased from 14ft 6in (4.42m) to 32ft (9.75m); 147TE (AQM-34Q), for medium-altitude surveillance with broad and long-span wings with tip pods, drop tanks and a data-link pod on the fin; and 147TF (AQM-34R), the second Combat (not Compass) Dawn model for SAC, which often carried underwing stores raising weight to 6,200lb (2,812kg), more than double the original value.

**Model 154** Developed under the USAF Compass Arrow programme, this model, AQM-91A, was assisted by North American (later Rockwell) for long overflights but these were halted in 1971. Popularly called Firefly, the AQM-91A was a large, 48ft (14.63m) span vehicle powered by a dorsal GE J97-3 of 5,270lb (2,390kg) thrust firing between twin fins. The Itek KA-80 optical bar panoramic camera was a massive installation with a rotating optical system eliminating the need to stop the lens at the end of each scan, taking 1,500 exposures each 45in (114.3cm) long and 4½in (11.4cm) wide with a resolution of 100 lines/mm.

**Model 234/239** These BGM-34 versions were developed for tactical strike and defence suppression. Major models were the 234 (BGM-34A), with a 1,700lb (771kg) J69-29 engine, firing Maverick, Shrike and Hobos mainly against ground radars; the 234A (BGM-34B), with a 1,920lb (871kg) J69-41A engine in a modified airframe, some with stabilised TV and laser designator and one with Hughes FLIR, used mainly in the "pathfinder" role to ▶

**Above: No other manufacturer can come anywhere near Teledyne Ryan Aeronautical in the scope and variety of its high-speed jet RPV programmes. The most prolific sub-family is the Model 147 (AQM-34, BQM-34, BGM-34), all of which were derived from the original Firebee I. This vehicle is a Model 147NC (AQM-34V) electronic-warfare platform, but several of the multisensor reconnaissance models are almost indistinguishable. This version can carry bulk EW dispenser pods under the wings, in the same way that reconnaissance Firebees are frequently operated with drop tanks.**

▶ designate targets for other RPVs; and the 239 (BGM-34C), a multimission version rebuilt from 147SCs strengthened for ground launch, with a weight of 6,000lb (2,722kg), and a span of 14ft 6in (4.42m), like other BGMs but with a long modular nose for recon, EW and strike.

**Model 255** AQM-34V is the latest EW version, some new built and 47 being updated AQM-34H and J, most delivered in 1976 to 11th TDS (Tac Drone Sqn) at Davis-Monthan. It has radio command guidance and carries underwing ALE-2 or ALE-38 chaff dispensers with an internal E-Systems Melpar active jammer. Normally launched by DC-130 and retrieved by CH-3 or -53.

### US Department of Defense

The US DoD has many RPV programmes. AMMR (Advanced Multi-Mission RPV), renamed ARPV (A for Advanced), was intended to replace Ryan's BGM-34C as a multimission vehicle with 20 or more in the same airspace

in the face of intensive jamming; the project was abandoned after much work by Boeing, Northrop and Rockwell. HASPA was a Navy project for a High-Altitude Superpressure Powered Aerostat, a 333ft (101m) electric/helium airship cruising at 68,000ft (20.72km) for ocean surveillance. Its successor is HiSpot (Hi-altitude Surveillance Platform for Over-the-horizon Targeting), now active at the Lockheed Missiles & Space Co, a 500ft (152m) airship using a hydrogen-fuelled propeller to hold station at 70,000ft (21.33km) for 100 days with 550lb (250kg) of sensors and equipment, including a giant internal aerial. LAMPS was a USAF scheme for a low-altitude multipurpose long-range RPV. Locust is one of the few surviving USAF programmes, for a low-cost expendable harassment vehicle to loiter over hostile air defences and draw fire, provoke radar silence and/or home in with an HE warhead on any emitter; Flight Dynamics Lab produced the XBM-106 and successor vehicles, using rate gyros allowing negative-*g* manoeuvres, while GD and TI are supplying sensors (German participation was ended—see Dornier—but that country is seen as a customer). Pave Tiger is a small canard with a pusher propeller being developed by Boeing to carry a USAF warhead or sensor/ECM payloads to specific high-priority targets, using sophisticated microprocessors, though Pave Tigers are expendable. RPAODS (Remotely Piloted Aerial Observation Designation System) was an Army effort that preceded Aquila (see Lockheed entry). TEDS (Tactical Expendable Drone System) was a USAF 1972–79 project which led to Pave Tiger. VLCHV (Very Low-Cost Harassment Vehicle) was a large programme, with many contractors, which preceded Locust.

# OTHER SUPER-VALUE MILITARY GUIDES IN THIS SERIES......

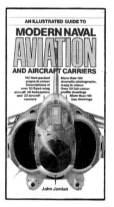

## OTHER ILLUSTRATED MILITARY GUIDES NOW AVAILABLE...

Allied Fighters of World War II
Bombers of World War II
German, Italian and Japanese Fighters
of World War II
Modern Fighters and
Attack Aircraft
Modern Soviet Navy

Modern Submarines
Modern Tanks
Modern US Navy
Modern Warships
Pistols and Revolvers
Rifles and Sub-Machine Guns
World War II Tanks

✻ Each has 160 fact-filled pages
✻ Each is colourfully illustrated with hundreds of action photographs
and technical drawings
✻ Each contains concisely presented data and accurate descriptions
of major international weapons
✻ Each represents tremendous value

**If you would like further information of any of our titles please write to:**

Publicity Dept. (Military Div.), Salamander Books Ltd.,
27 Old Gloucester Street, London WC1N 3AF

PRINTED IN BELGIUM BY
INTERNATIONAL BOOK PRODUCTION